D0352124

JUSTIN POLLARD

Justin Pollard read archaeology and anthropology at Cambridge. He is an historical writer and consultant in film and TV. His credits include the films *Elizabeth* and *Atonement* and the BBC TV Drama *The Tudors*, as well as more than twenty-five documentary series such as Channel 4's *Time Team*. He is a writer and researcher for *QI* and the author of seven books including *The Interesting Bits* and *Secret Britain*.

Also by Justin Pollard

Seven Ages of Britain
Alfred the Great
The Rise and Fall of Alexandria
The Interesting Bits
Charge!
Secret Britain

BOFFINOLOGY

JUSTIN POLLARD

The Real Stories Behind Our
Greatest Scientific Discoveries

JOHN MURRAY

First published in Great Britain in 2010 by John Murray (Publishers)
An Hachette UK Company

First published in paperback in 2011

1

© Justin Pollard 2010

The right of Justin Pollard to be identified as the Author of the Work has been
asserted by him in accordance with the Copyright, Designs and Patents Act 1988.

All rights reserved. Apart from any use permitted under UK copyright
law no part of this publication may be reproduced, stored in a retrieval system,
or transmitted, in any form or by any means without the prior written permission
of the publisher, nor be otherwise circulated in any form of binding or cover other
than that in which it is published and without a similar condition being
imposed on the subsequent purchaser.

A CIP catalogue record for this title is available from the British Library

ISBN 978-1-84854-201-3

Typeset in Sabon MT by Palimpsest Book Production Ltd,
Falkirk, Stirlingshire

Printed and bound by Clays Ltd, St Ives plc

John Murray policy is to use papers that are natural, renewable and recyclable
products and made from wood grown in sustainable forests. The logging and
manufacturing processes are expected to conform to the environmental
regulations of the country of origin.

John Murray (Publishers)
338 Euston Road
London NW1 3BH

www.johnmurray.co.uk

For Fliss who arrived just as I started this book
and for Connie who waited so long for a little sister.

The essence of science: ask an impertinent question,
and you are on the way to a pertinent answer.
Jacob Bronowski, *The Ascent of Man* (1973)

Contents

Introduction

When I was a child there always seemed something perfect about science. It was carried out by brilliant people in immaculate white coats who would invent audacious experiments leading, inevitably, to stunning results. In this way science would take another giant step forward, the scientists would congratulate one another, then clear their benches and start all over again, on a new and even harder problem.

Obviously this wasn't my personal experience of science, which more often involved not completely understanding the instructions in science classes, messing up the experiment and then fiddling the results to fit in with what I thought was probably being asked.

That was unless the experiment involved explosives. I loved explosives (in a wholly peaceful way, you understand) and in those fondly remembered days of youth you could still buy in our local chemist's shop all the necessary ingredients for making gunpowder. I didn't mess up experiments making rockets, not after a batch of gunpowder I was preparing accidentally combusted, removing an eyebrow and leaving a large hole in the carpet. Fortunately, like all good scientists, I'd taken precautions and had been preparing the explosive in my sister's room, so it was her carpet that bought it.

Making firework rockets was about as close as I ever got to being one of those perfect scientists I imagined, working away silently, diligently and alone, slowly preparing for the key experiment, the moment when the fuse was lit and the great adventure began. In truth it was sometimes a rather disappointing adventure as I made quite a lot of damp squibs. It was also sometimes very alarming as my rudimentary knowledge of aerodynamics often led to my rockets being a touch unstable and they were more likely to shoot off into next door's hedge than to rise majestically into the air. But sometimes it really, really worked and the rocket whooshed off the little Meccano gantry I'd built and up into the blue skies of childhood. That was magical. That was what it was like to be a real scientist.

And so I studied, and I built rockets, and I peered at the big universe through my telescope and at the small universe through my microscope, and finally I became – an historian. Not really what I had planned. Of course the American chemist Frank Westheimer once observed: 'Surprisingly, history is much more difficult than chemistry,' but I think he was fibbing. Today I do my science vicariously, through the pages of *New Scientist* and *Nature* and Ben Goldacre's 'Bad Science' column, and I sometimes have the privilege of talking to real scientists through my researches for the BBC series *QI*.

But if I cannot claim to do real science myself, as a historian I do at least get to spend a lot of time with dead scientists. There are thousands of them in history books and reading the stories of their lives has taught me something about science itself. Real science is not done by the perfect white-coated men and women I imagined as a child. It does have its heroes, of course, but it also has its villains, its disasters, its brilliant ideas that turn suddenly to dust and those handfuls of dust that, quite unexpectedly, lead to moments of genius. There is just more chaos in science than I ever imagined in my youth. It is a field populated by humans, together with all their triumphs and failings, their valiant strivings, their dogged determination, their indomitable spirit and their bitter rivalries, prejudices and tempers. That is what this book is about.

Boffinology is not meant to be encyclopaedic or in any way a 'history of science'. Rather it is simply a collection of 100 stories found by an historian who nearly became a scientist and who thought they helped to explain, at least to him, what science is, where it has come from and what it's like to actually do. Science is often seen as not being about scientists; it is about their work, not them. But, in truth, all science comes out of who those people are. I hope here to put some of the characters, good and bad, back into their stories. Perhaps one might inspire you to become a chemist, but I hope none of them inspires you to become a poisoner. Both can be found in these pages, though, for good measure.

I doubt whether every one will be new to you. If you are a physicist you might find the physics stories familiar – they are the kind of thing physicists tell, after all – but perhaps the stories from the other sciences will still surprise you. The same goes for all the disciplines. Each one has also been kept deliberately short, so that you might read one or another here or there, whenever you fancy. They have been presented in the order in which you read them for a reason but you don't have to keep to it. If you'd like to know more, there are whole books written about each one. I know; I read them.

Most of all, I hope these stories are memorable. They have stayed with me for over twenty years of research, beginning not long after I built my last childhood rocket, and they remain with me as I wonder today whether I'll ever be allowed to build rockets with my own children. On the off chance that I won't, these 100 tales may have to stand in their stead. At least that way the carpets will be safe.

1

The Great Adventure

(In which we look at the origins and process of
science, how one thing leads to another and how
the latter is sometimes stolen by someone who
had precious little to do with the former.)

*The world looks so different after learning science. For
example, trees are made of air, primarily. When they are
burned, they go back to air, and in the flaming heat is
released the flaming heat of the sun which was bound in to
convert the air into tree.*

Richard Feynman, *speech to the fifteenth annual meeting
of the National Science Teachers Association,*
New York City (1966)

～

Thales of Miletus is often considered the
father of modern science and so it's only fair
that we should start with him when this book,
after all, deals with the ideas and products of
so many of his intellectual descendants. But
it must also be said that he provides a
rather unusual role model.

～

A cautionary tale

There are two problems with Thales. The first is that he never
wrote anything down or, if he did, it certainly hasn't survived.
As a result we're forced to rely on accounts written hundreds
of years after his death, which have a nasty habit of not really
agreeing with each other at all.

The second problem is that every thought, every science and
every philosophy needs a beginning. In the absence of firm
evidence, many a scientist and philosopher has laid that origin
at Thales's door, crediting him not just with inventing 'science'
but with most of Western thought.

So what do we know about this man from whom all the
other ideas in this book flow? First, he really did exist, which
is a start, and lived roughly from the mid-620s BC to the
mid-540s BC. He was probably born in Miletus on the west
coast of Asia Minor and may have been somewhere between
seventy-eight and ninety when he died, which was a good innings
for those days.

After that it gets a shade hazy. Our main source for Thales's
life is the Greek historian Herodotus writing about a hundred
years later, the philosopher Aristotle writing another hundred

years after that, and the slightly unreliable and wholly unsourced Diogenes Laërtius writing perhaps 600 years after that. All agree that he was one of the 'Seven Sages of Greece', a title given to seven statesmen, philosophers and lawmakers later renowned for their wisdom, even though historians don't agree who the rest of those seven were.

All, however, are keen to flesh out this rather distant story with a few anecdotes. According to Herodotus, one of Thales's great tricks was to predict a solar eclipse, one of which we now know occurred on 28 May 585 BC. It just so happened that a large battle (the battle of Halys) was happening at the time between the Lydians (under the wealthy King Croesus) and the Medes. Both sides were so impressed with his prediction that they immediately downed swords and declared peace. Croesus then marched on Persia but came to a grinding halt at a river too wide to cross. Quick as a flash, Thales suggested diverting the river upstream so that half of it started to flow behind the army. This shrank the river ahead and made it fordable.

There are many other such tales, including how he bought the option to use all Miletus's olive presses for one season, having correctly predicted a bumper harvest – making him the first options trader in history. He is also credited with discovering Thales's Theorem, a rather nifty piece of geometry that states that if A, B and C are points on a circle and the line AC is the diameter, the angle ABC is always a right angle. For this he has been called the first true mathematician and he remains the earliest person to have a mathematical discovery attributed to them.

You're probably thinking this sounds a bit like hearsay and not very scientific at all. And you'd be right. If we want to learn what was really special about Thales, we need to look at what Aristotle has to say about him.

Aristotle said that Thales thought that the world originates from and returns to water – or, to put it another way, everything is made from water, or is 'transformed' from water. This seems unpromising at first, as unpromising as Anaximenes's contention that everything is made from air, but it hides at its core the foundation of all science. Before Thales, the answer to what everything was made of, where it came from and where it was going to end up was simple: God, or, rather, the gods. Thales's watery idea may have been, to modern eyes, a touch off beam, but it marks the first time in Western thought that anyone rejected a mystical explanation of phenomena in favour of looking for natural causes. Furthermore he was the first person to attempt to explore this new way of thinking by trying to define general principles in the world around him and to come up with hypotheses to test them. This marks the very beginning of science.

That is, of course, if Aristotle isn't making it up, which he may well be. Aristotle, like so many others, was looking for an origin for his own ideas and may simply have put these words into Thales's mouth. Somewhere, perhaps during Thales's lifetime, someone – maybe even Thales himself – did have this momentous thought, but Aristotle's story is, sadly, no more reliable than another told by Diogenes Laërtius. He claims that one evening Thales was led out of his house by an old woman so he could study the stars. It being a dark night and Thales being old, he fell into a ditch but received precious little sympathy. Instead the old woman berated him, saying: 'Do you, O Thales, who cannot see what is under your feet, think you shall understand what is in heaven?'

And that is a warning any prospective boffin would do well to heed.

∽

There are a lot of pitfalls in science beside
the literal ones that Thales used to fall into.
For one thing, science is more often a collabora-
tive effort than a solo performance, but many of
those involved seem painfully unaware of this.
Ideas have value and precedence in a discovery
is everything, as the story of the unravelling
of the properties of water shows.

∽

The water board

This story, which involves three very different characters, is not
only tortuous but involves the untimely death of one of its protagonists. After Thales – known as 'the father of science' – rather
sweepingly suggested that everything was water, there was a
2,200-year gap in progress before someone came along who
might discover what water itself was actually made of.

Henry Cavendish was just as absent-minded as Thales (see
page 7) but he was also chronically shy, particularly when it
came to speaking to women. In fact, he was absolutely terrified
of them and would communicate with his female servants only
via written notes.

Cavendish was one of a new breed of eighteenth-century
'gentleman scientists' – men who dedicated their otherwise easy
lives and considerable financial resources to investigating the
nature of things. In Cavendish's case his interests lay mainly in
the measuring of electric current and the 'capturing of fractious
airs'. The system he devised for measuring electric current did
not catch on, as it involved shocking himself and making a
relative estimation of the degree of pain this caused.

When it came to fractious airs, however, Cavendish was a genius. By fractioning off gases from air, in much the same way that petrol is fractioned off from crude oil, he identified the 'fixed air'. Although this didn't seem to achieve much by itself, it also isolated (in 1766) a much rarer 'inflammable' air, which was a lot more lively. Several aspects of this gas had hooked his interest. First, this strange stuff was lighter than air; second, it had a habit of exploding when you put a match to it; and third, and most interestingly of all, when you did set fire to it in a closed container, the walls became covered with what Cavendish called 'dew' – a substance that he thought was probably water.

Cavendish, with his reclusive nature, didn't take the credit for this impressive discovery. In fact, he took hardly any credit for any of his experiments as he was never bold enough to publish a single book (just twenty short papers). To explain to the world what he had discovered would require the impressive intellect and moral ambivalence of a man who began his scientific career with the statement: 'I am young and eager for glory.'

The speaker was Antoine-Laurent de Lavoisier, a French contemporary of Cavendish's who is today described as 'the father of modern chemistry' – a title that would have made Cavendish go puce and hide in a corner but which Lavoisier would have loved.

Lavoisier was brilliant and dashing – not only marrying a beautiful thirteen-year-old prodigy but putting her to work translating English scientific papers for him, for the simple reason that, for all his brilliance, he was not averse to a little cheating wherever possible. As his own biographer delicately puts it: 'This tendency to use the results of others without acknowledgment then draw conclusions was characteristic of Lavoisier.'

Amongst those papers that Madame Lavoisier translated was Cavendish's report on 'inflammable air', which caught the Frenchman's attention. Repeating his colleague's experiment on fractioning air, he too isolated the 'flammable' fraction but made the key addition of giving this fraction its own name – hydrogen. Lavoisier is credited with the discovery of hydrogen even though he copied the experiment out of a book. Schoolboys have been trying to emulate his success ever since.

Of course hydrogen is only half the story of the properties of water, but Lavoisier was not averse to 'borrowing' his way to victory with the other half. Back in England around this time another gentleman scientist, one Joseph Priestley (see page 147) was also investigating air. Priestley was a great experimenter, but like Cavendish he wasn't good with names. During his experiments he'd isolated carbon dioxide, which he rather drily called 'fixed air'. As a byproduct he realised that he could dissolve this in water to make it fizzy, so he should be credited as the father of all soda drinks. It may not be as good as being the 'father of science', or even the 'father of chemistry', but it's a start.

He also identified what he called 'phlogisticated nitrous air', which was particularly difficult to say after you'd sniffed it, as it's more commonly known as laughing gas. Most importantly, he discovered 'dephlogisticated air', a name that failed to catch on, allowing the ever-watchful Lavoisier to copy Priestley's experiment, just as he had done with Cavendish's, to name the resulting gas (which he called 'oxygen') and claim to be its discoverer.

Both Cavendish and Priestley had noticed that burning 'inflammable air' created 'dew' but it was Lavoisier who now had the evidence and the names to describe it properly for the first time. This he did, declaring that water must be made of a combination of his two newly discovered gases, hydrogen and oxygen, which it is.

The last laugh in this story of chemical espionage goes, appropriately enough, to the nitrous-oxide-sniffing Englishman. Priestley was a devout Unitarian preacher and a strong supporter of the French Revolution. Indeed, so keen was he that, having done his best to whip up discontent amongst the French (and the English) peasantry, he felt it wise to emigrate with his family to the USA. Lavoisier, the aristocratic father of modern chemistry and the first man to deconstruct water, failed to make such a tactical withdrawal. He was guillotined.

⁓

Water would, of course, go on to
become the power behind the Industrial
Revolution but the story behind the inventions
that exploited science's discoveries is often no
clearer than the story of the discovery itself.
Witness the steam engine . . .

⁓

Who invented the steam engine?

There was a time, not that long ago, when every British schoolchild knew the answer to this simple question. The steam engine, as school books proudly told, was invented by the Scotsman James Watt. Or was it Thomas Newcomen? But even putting aside for the moment the claim of Hero of Alexandria (see page 294) to have invented the steam engine in the first century AD, we need to do more than narrow it down to these two in order to tell the whole story.

The saga of the modern steam engine should perhaps begin with Blasco de Garay, a naval officer in Charles V's Spain. By 1543, Charles V had every reason to fear water in its liquid form. Only the previous year when his fleet was off Algiers a fierce storm had wrecked fifteen of his warships and 140 transports, drowning 8,000 men and nearly drowning Charles himself. Now when he heard of Garay's proposal for a ship that could move against tide and wind at will, he commissioned a test with his own vessel *Trinity*. According to the surviving account this was fitted with a steam boiler and promptly motored up and down, much to the delight of Charles.

As with everything to do with steam, however, nothing is what it seems. First, the 'authentic account' of this impressive trial wasn't written down until 1825 and may well be forged. Second, and rather handily for all concerned, it states that Blasco refused to explain how his machine worked; as soon as the trial was over, he packed it all up and took it away, never to be seen again. Thanks to his own secrecy, we'll never know whether or not he was the true inventor of the steam engine.

The British, who were considerably less bashful, maintain that it was their Thomas Newcomen who invented the steam engine. Well, not quite. By the end of the seventeenth century the British did at least have a good reason for needing to invent some form of engine. Mining – for iron, coal and tin – was really taking off and mines had an unpleasant habit of filling with groundwater, which happens to make up 99 per cent of all the fresh water available on earth. At this time the donkey work of pumping it out involved real donkeys and buckets, and this was an age when donkeys and buckets were expensive, so Thomas Newcomen addressed himself to finding a solution.

Newcomen was an inventor in the days when, unless you were an aristocrat with a lot of time on your hands, being a 'scientist' wasn't considered to be a good job. Coming from rather humble Devonport stock, he was of a class known as 'schemers' and was generally referred to as a 'blacksmith', although he preferred the term 'ironmonger', displaying an early case of 'status anxiety'. Newcomen went to the mines of Cornwall to study the problem of pumping water out of deep diggings. Despite his being described as the 'father of the steam engine', one of the first things he came across there was . . . a steam engine.

It had been built by Thomas Savery, who describes it in his book *An Engine to Raise Water by Fire*. Savery, who was much posher than Newcomen, basked in the grand title of 'military engineer', although that didn't stop the aristocracy, who were running the show, from snubbing him. When he suggested to the Admiralty a novel little idea he'd had for propelling a ship using paddle wheels, they replied loftily that they couldn't see why they should 'have interloping people, that have no concern with us, to pretend to contrive or invent things for us'.

Savery built his ship anyway and paddled it up and down the Thames. Unfortunately for him, no one important seems to have been watching on this occasion, so he turned his skills to inventing an engine for pumping out mines. Well that depends to some degree on your definition of 'inventing'. There are rumours that Savery based his work on the writings of Edward Somerset, 2nd Marquess of Worcester, who a century earlier had been pondering the knotty problem of perpetual motion. Another possible 'inventor' of the steam engine, Jean Théophile Desaguliers (who, despite his name, was English), claimed that Savery had not only read Worcester's book but had bought up all the copies available and burnt them in order to claim to have invented the engine himself. Furthermore, there was the fact that Savery had certainly based his boiler on the Frenchman Denis Papin's 'Digester' or 'pressure cooker' of 1679.

Even if Savery did borrow and improve other people's ideas, he can still be credited with first building in practice what Worcester called his 'semi-omnipotent and water commanding engine'. Having perfected his model, he proudly displayed it in 1689 to King William III at Hampton Court who immediately granted him a patent.

That was the start of his difficulties. First, he decided to call his invention a 'fire engine', which confused everybody, although he later changed this to 'The Miner's Friend'. His real problem, however, was that his engines were underpowered and used a huge amount of fuel to lift a small quantity of water. In short, donkeys and buckets were better. Mine owners were also frightened that his great hissing boilers might explode – which of course they did. Even after they had been fitted with pressure valves (invented by Desaguliers), they could still go wrong because operators were in the habit of putting weights on the valves to create more steam pressure and get their job done more quickly. This was usually the last bright idea they ever had.

It was Thomas Newcomen who realised that Savery had gone about the whole business back to front. Savery had used steam pressure to push a plunger up a piston. This meant you needed high steam pressure in boilers, which tended to lead to explosions, as welding was still in its infancy. Newcomen turned this idea on its head by inventing the 'atmospheric engine', which gained its power not from steam pressure but from the huge pressure of the atmosphere all around us. Newcomen filled a piston with steam and then suddenly cooled it, using water, making the steam condense out and creating a partial vacuum in the piston tube, which in turn led to the external atmospheric pressure pushing the piston back down again. Atmospheric pressure is enormous compared to the pressure in a 'Papin Pressure Cooker', so his engine was much more powerful as well as much safer.

And was the world impressed? No. Desaguliers grudgingly admitted that Newcomen and his partner John Calley had found a good solution but added: 'not being either philosophers to understand the reason, or mathematicians enough to calculate the powers and proportions of the parts, they very luckily, by accident, found what they sought for'.

The celebrated 'Lunatick' Robert Hooke (see page 19) – father of the modern microscope and inventor of the biological term 'cell' – who had been told of the project early on by Newcomen, was even more dismissive and told them they should never have proceeded with the idea in the first place. Perhaps Hooke was trying to buy time for his friend, the Dutch astronomer Christian Huygens, who had designed an engine driven by gunpowder instead of steam. Then again perhaps Hooke was just experiencing a moment of madness. He was, after all, the designer of the notorious Bethlehem hospital lunatic asylum, better known as 'Bedlam'.

However, miners – as well as borough councils that needed fresh water for their burgeoning urban populations – did take note and the Newcomen engine, after various tinkerings, became the first great workhorse of the Industrial Revolution – that is, until James Watt (see page 20) came along.

A mathematical instrument maker, Watt is often credited with inventing the steam engine, which, as we've just seen, he can't possibly have done. What he did do was invent the separate condenser, which allowed the steam to be cooled outside the piston, making the whole operation far more efficient. He also invented the 'flyball governor', which controls the speed of a steam engine and whose positive feedback principle represents the first piece of true 'automation' in any modern machine. Not content with all this, he also had a unit of electricity named after him and, perhaps most importantly of all, coined the term by which the Industrial Revolution was measured: horsepower.

It was at this point that Richard Trevithick came on the scene. Now that the basic operation of the Newcomen engine, as improved by Watt, had been established, Trevithick applied himself to making it go faster and harder – the beginnings of the endless industrial quest for horsepower – a term he could thankfully now use. Newcomen had invented the atmospheric engine to avoid the need for the high-pressure steam that had powered Savery's engine but Trevithick turned this notion on its head by introducing a high-pressure, Newcomen-style engine. Watt had considered doing this himself but was still unsure about how far welding technology had progressed.

With his new high-pressure engine, Trevithick set about freeing the steam engine from its pithead moorings and in 1802 built what is claimed to be the world's first automobile – a steam-operated car that was rather unfortunately known as 'The Puffing Devil'. In fact Nicolas-Joseph Cugnot probably invented the automobile in 1769 when his 'steam wagon' first ran. In 1771 it ran straight into a brick wall, making Cugnot also the first man ever to have a car accident. Regardless of who invented the car, everyone thought it a stupid invention that would never take off, so Trevithick turned his attention to another type of locomotion – the train.

Horse-drawn trains had been pulling wagons on rails out of mine workings since before Savery had been pumping water out of them, but no one had thought of replacing the flesh-and-blood horse with an iron horse. Trevithick did, and thanks to his high-pressure engine he succeeded in building the world's first locomotive, which he forgot to name. Had he done so, he might have remained as famous as a certain George Stephenson who, inspired by his work, built a locomotive with the dashing name of *Rocket*.

Of course, not all scientists have worked
in bitter opposition. The wiser amongst them
have formed clubs for mutual support, the free
exchange of ideas and the odd good dinner.
Such a sensible idea could only come
from a bunch of Lunaticks.

The Lunaticks

Modern learned societies owe their origins to the development, in the sixteenth century, of networks of European astronomers, natural philosophers and mathematicians who, though never formally members of the same educational institution, formed a sort of ad hoc college, bound together by the notes and treatises they passed amongst themselves. Just a century later this had been formalised in Britain into a group of corresponding scientists including Robert Hooke (see page 201), John Evelyn, Christopher Wren and Robert Boyle (see page 75), who referred to themselves as 'The Invisible College'.

In time the Invisible College itself transmogrified into the first learned scientific society to receive a royal charter – the Royal Society of London for the Improvement of Natural Knowledge, which rapidly became so famous that it was soon known simply as 'The Royal Society'. From this seed grew a plethora of other scientific societies, many less formal or more specialised, some for those gentlemen scientists in the provinces or abroad, and others for those who might not quite 'suit' the grander institutions.

Amongst this latter group in the eighteenth century there emerged one of the strangest and yet most influential groups of all. The Lunar Society was far less formal than its royal counterpart; indeed, it was so informal that it had no constitution and no real method of either electing or deselecting members; it never published anything, and never kept minutes of meetings or a list of members. Some historians have struggled with the idea that it even existed or, if it did, who actually belonged to it.

The Lunar Society, whose members originally referred to themselves simply as 'fellow-schemers', was a very different beast to the Royal Society, being based around a group of intellectuals who eventually found a home in the new industrial heartland of England – Birmingham. These men were practical scientists and manufacturers rather than the gentlemen scientists of other societies, although some did later gain admission to those more illustrious bodies. Their informal group was founded as a dining society and got its name from their habit of meeting from 2 p.m. to 8 p.m. on days when there was a full moon, whose light would make for a safer journey home after the meeting.

The great strength of the group was that they were not all of the same profession. In the latter part of the eighteenth century, the sciences and the individual disciplines within them had not yet been separated out. As a result the Lunar Society was a wide cross-section of people who might have professional interests in one area and amateur hobbies in another.

Amongst its members was the potter Josiah Wedgwood, one of the first men to turn ceramic production into a modern industry. He might find himself at a Lunar dinner sitting next to Thomas Jefferson's old teacher William Small, steam pioneer James Watt (see page 13) or his business partner Matthew Boulton at whose house the meetings often took place. Samuel Galton Jnr, who, unusually for a pacifist Quaker, was a gun manufacturer, might find himself talking politics with slavery abolitionist James Day, whilst chemist and inventor of the fizzy drink Joseph Priestley (see page 12) could be found in discussion with William Withering, the discoverer of the heart drug digitalis. Erasmus Darwin, Charles's grandfather and a man who had turned down George III's offer to become royal physician, might also be found reading letters from corresponding members who included the discoverer of Uranus, William Herschel, the botanist and member of Captain Cook's first expedition Joseph Banks, the chemist Antoine-Laurent de Lavoisier (see page 11) and amateur electrician Benjamin Franklin (see page 28).

Of course no group bound largely by the ties of friendship could last for ever. As the members grew older and died, the Lunar Society ceased to be very active in the 1790s and was closed down altogether around 1813 although, typically, no one can quite determine the exact date. Most former members had died by 1820, which certainly reduced their activity.

It is also a matter for debate whether a group that never issued a society publication would be capable of leaving a legacy of any kind. However, what mattered for the Lunar Society members was not the publication record but the opportunity to mix with others whose interests varied greatly from their own and from whose input their own studies might be improved. Did Erasmus Darwin's discussions with the early geologists later influence his grandson Charles? It is hard to be certain, but this most eclectic of clubs formed the crucible in which a sizeable part of modern Britain was formed. That being the case, it is perhaps not surprising that the members referred to themselves, informally at least, as 'Lunaticks'.

∽

Whether the scientist is a Lunatick or a loner, some science requires a degree of bravery. When cartoonists draw scientists they rarely have bulging muscles and a knife clenched in their teeth, but not all science can be done in the comfort of the laboratory. Sometimes it can be very dangerous indeed.

∽

The hardest metre

The metre is one of the foundations of modern science – the unit of length that marks the fixed point from which other measurements are derived. But discovering its precise measurement proved no picnic.

For the French Academy of Sciences the measurement was simple – they defined the metre as one ten-millionth of the distance from the North Pole to the Equator along the Paris meridian. The difficulty was that the Bureau des Longitudes needed to know how far that actually was, and with astonishing accuracy.

The work of surveying this distance had been begun in 1792 but had ground to a halt in 1804 following the death of one of the main protagonists. Now, in 1806, two new men were chosen to complete the task – Jean-Baptiste Biot and Dominique François Jean Arago. Their job was to survey their way down France and through Spain to find the precise latitudes of a number of places, including Formentera in the Balearic Islands, and hence measure a known section of the meridian arc. This involved triangulating their position from the tops of mountains and hills.

Thus in 1806 they found themselves on top of a hill on the Mediterranean coast near Denia in Spain, from which they needed to take measurements across to the Balearic Islands, which lie near by. As making observations across the water to misty mountaintops proved tricky, they decided the best method might be to send one of the party across to the islands who would ascend the mountaintop to be measured and light a bonfire at the summit at night. This single, clear light could then easily be seen from their current position.

With this ingenious solution, the surveying progressed rather well. Biot and Arago leapfrogged from Denia to Ibiza, and from Ibiza to Formentera, lighting fires as they went. Finally they arrived on Mallorca where Biot, in late 1807, bade his partner farewell and headed back to Paris with their preliminary observations.

Arago meanwhile continued the work, choosing the summit of Mola de S'Eslop as a base, on which he built a small stone hut to live in and a large bonfire to signal to his assistants across the water. So things proceeded happily until June 1808 when, rather unfortunately, the Peninsular War broke out between France and Spain. What had until then been no more than an eccentric sight – a Frenchman lighting nightly fires on a hilltop – now began to worry the Mallorcans. Clearly under the impression that Arago was a French spy signalling the enemy, they cheerfully reported him to the army, which sent a detachment of troops to arrest him. Fortunately for Arago he spoke fluent Mallorquin. When he bumped into his potential captors as he was coming down the mountain, he urged them to continue on to the top where, he told them, the spy was still at work. The ploy worked at least for a while but in Palma he was too well known. Forced to give himself up, he was sent to the Bellver Castle prison.

There are two versions of what happened next. Either he managed to persuade his captors that he was no threat or he escaped. One way or another, on 28 July he found himself in a fishing boat bound for Algiers. It had all been a little too eventful for a peaceful surveyor and so in Algiers Arago immediately took ship for Marseilles, hoping to return to Paris as quickly as possible. Just as the ship approached its destination it was attacked by Spanish pirates and the hapless Arago was again captured, this time being taken to Roses in Catalonia, where he again found himself imprisoned, this time in a windmill.

By now Arago was a bit fed up with the trials of surveying in a war zone and was delighted when Roses fell to the French, although his joy proved premature. As part of an apparently Algerian party he was not released but simply transferred to another prison, this time in Palamos. The French were busy fighting a war and so what they considered to be foreign prisoners could wait. Eventually, it was the Dey of Algiers who proved the Frenchman's saviour, demanding the return of his sailors. The bemused Arago was sent back with them.

Not that they made it back to Algiers. Just off the coast a northerly wind blew up and drove their vessel into the village of Bougie. Here the captain told Arago that the winter weather (it was now December 1808) made a sea crossing impossible and they would have to wait for the spring. Arago, not surprisingly, was getting a shade impatient and opted to walk back to Algiers where he might find a captain willing to take him home.

This would have been a good idea were it not for the fact that the inhabitants of Algiers were cross with the French who, in the excitement of war, had failed to pay for materials exported to France. When this angry Frenchman arrived in the port, the Algerians saw a suitable scapegoat, promptly arrested him and held him for ransom.

It was June 1809 by the time payments were made and Arago was at last released. This time he did make his way back to

Marseilles where, to add one last insult, he was quarantined in a hospital for infectious diseases. Fortunately this would prove his last imprisonment and he finally reached Paris, where a hero's welcome awaited.

The measurements he had faithfully carried with him throughout his travails helped to define the exact length of a metre. Jules Verne would later fictionalise his friend Arago's adventures in *Off on a Comet* and it is thanks to his novel that a monument now stands at one of Arago and Biot's bonfire sites on Formentera. Ironically the monument is not to poor, long-suffering Arago but to Jules Verne, who probably never even visited the island.

❧

Just as we can't confine scientists to their
lab, so we can't always confine them to the
small world of one discipline or sub-discipline.
Occasionally they escape out into the real
world and put their particular skills to
a surprising, even deadly, use.

❧

Newton down the pub

Isaac Newton is remembered today largely for describing the action of gravity or, perhaps amongst the more numerate, for calculus, although not amongst numerate Germans who think their man Leibniz (see pages 78 and 197) should really take the credit. Yet Newton's life was not one of pure abstract research; for thirty-one years he had a government job that involved his spending an inordinate amount of time heavily disguised in some of London's 'livelier' inns.

Newton was not himself one for the high life. His secretary once commented that he had seen the great man laugh only once in five years, and that was when someone asked him what the point was in reading Euclid (see page 203). Following the publication of his great work, *Philosophiæ Naturalis Principia Mathematica* (often known simply as the *Principia*), he became a regular government 'expert', which led to an unusual offer of employment.

In 1695 the government co-opted Newton and seven other dignitaries to look into one of its more pressing difficulties. The country was at war with France and therefore in a financial quandary, a situation not helped by the fact that her coinage was slowly and quite literally being eroded. The currency in everyday use was made of bullion silver but had poorly defined edges. 'Clippers' would illegally snip the edges off the coins to sell the silver. As a coin was supposedly worth the value of the silver in it, this was devaluing the currency.

Newton and his committee reported back that the only solution was a recoinage – that is, taking back all the old money and reminting it as new coins worth their actual value in silver. The government agreed and the recoinage began, which should have been an end to Newton's involvement. However, the chancellor of the exchequer wanted to thank Newton for his work so he did what all governments of the day did: he offered him a sinecure – a government job with a salary but no duties, or none that he couldn't get someone else to do.

Newton was the last man to take any job lightly, even one meant just to provide him with a bit of pocket money. He accepted the post of Warden of the Mint but, much to everyone's surprise, he also actually did the work. Seizing control of the recoinage, he determined to beat the clippers. All his new coinage was to have a clearly defined edge so that any clipping would instantly be exposed. To that end all silver coins were to be 'milled' with a series of vertical grooves on their edge. As a further precaution Newton decided to set an inscription on the coin that would not only add to its decorative value but act as a deterrent to the edges being shaved off. That legend, which still appears on some UK coins today, was 'Decus et Tutamen' – 'an ornament and a safeguard'.

With clipping in decline, many of its former practitioners turned instead to coining – or outright counterfeiting. Technically, the position of Warden of the Mint also involved actually catching these criminals and so, after some initial misgivings, Newton threw himself into that as well. Clippers and coiners were not the sort of people you'd meet of an evening at his more usual haunt, the Royal Society, so Newton donned a disguise and hung around London's least salubrious pubs, hoping to overhear their plottings.

And overhear them he did. At great personal risk Newton pursued London's criminal underworld, most notably in the form of William Chaloner, a former quack doctor, confidence trickster and the first coiner to perfect edge milling on his fake coins. Chaloner was a cut above most coiners, even offering his services to the government as the only man who could stop counterfeiting – and he had a point as, if anyone knew how it was done, it was him. Going further, he claimed the Royal Mint, under Newton's control, was riddled with corruption, lending out its dies and issuing underweight coins, and he threatened to 'pursue that old Dogg the Warden to the end so long as he lived'.

Now Newton was a man whose temper could occasionally get the better of him. In a fit of pique, aged just nineteen, he had threatened to burn down his mother and stepfather's house – with them in it. Not surprisingly, he was apoplectic about Chaloner's claim and put to use all the methodical practices that had aided him in his scientific work, setting up an extensive network of spies and informers to catch out the ever-bolder coiner.

By January 1699, Newton had cornered every accomplice and crony from every era of Chaloner's life from every back-street bar in London. His investigation complete, Chaloner was arrested. The charge was treason, a penalty Chaloner himself had exhorted the government to apply to coining at a time when he hoped to become their official 'expert' on the subject. The meticulous Newton had gathered witnesses from throughout the coiner's career, who were paraded in court before the astonished defendant, who had elected to conduct his own defence, unaware of the lengths to which Newton had gone. So panicked was Chaloner that he tried feigning madness and when this failed he was reduced to simply insulting each witness in turn. The result was a foregone conclusion and he was sentenced to death.

In the two weeks before sentence was carried out, he wrote a series of letters to Newton, some abusive, some begging for mercy, his last pitiful note saying: 'O Dear Sr do this mercifull deed O my offending you has brought this upon me O for Gods sake if not mine Keep me from being murdered O dear Sr nobody can save me but you O God my God I shall be murdered unless you save me O I hope God will move your heart with mercy pitty to do this thing for me,' and signing himself: 'I am Your near murdered humble Servant.'

A vengeful Newton was not moved to pity. Those who had crossed him in the scientific community could have told Chaloner that he would never forget a grudge. If even his colleagues could not seek forgiveness for imagined academic sins, what chance had a notorious criminal?

William Chaloner was dragged on a hurdle to Tyburn on 16 March 1699 where he was hanged. As a traitor, he was denied even the right to face his death in an insulating haze of alcohol. That December, Newton was granted one of the most lucrative offices in the gift of the state as Master of the Mint.

⌒⌒

Out in the real world science has a nasty
habit of coming into contact with politics,
not always with edifying results.

⌒⌒

The war of the knobs and the points

Benjamin Franklin, when he wasn't making American history, was a noted electrical experimenter. In the latter role, one of his great contributions to the modern world has been his invention of the lightning conductor. What is less well known, perhaps, is how this led to a war.

Franklin's electrical experiments had shown that conductors with a sharp point apparently discharged electricity more quietly and over a greater distance than those that were blunter. This gave him the idea of putting sharp conducting iron points on tall buildings and attaching these to a wire passing down to the earth and so, as he put it, 'drawing the electrical fire silently out of a cloud before it came nigh enough to strike, and thereby secure us from that most sudden and terrible mischief'.

This seemed perfectly reasonable and soon the Philadelphia State House was sporting its own gilded iron lightning conductor. The concept rapidly crossed the Atlantic and was eagerly taken up by those with a particular interest in avoiding lightning, notably the owners of churches and cathedrals with large spires, as well as those who worked in gunpowder magazines.

However, not everyone was delighted with the idea. The great French electrical experimenter Abbé Nollet solemnly warned the French Academy of Sciences: 'I believe that they [lightning conductors] are more suitable to attract the fire of thunder to us than to preserve us from it.' Such sudden concern for his fellow man was admirable coming from someone who attempted to measure the 'speed of electricity' by discharging a huge shock through a series of connected monks and noting the rate at which they jumped in the air.

In England the invention was taken more seriously and, after the church of St Bride's on Fleet Street was badly damaged by a lightning strike, St Paul's Cathedral was quickly fitted with one of Franklin's 'points'. The government was also interested and a Royal Society commission suggested the installation of pointed conductors on the roof of the gunpowder magazine of the Board of Ordnance House at Purfleet, which was duly done.

Then disaster struck. In 1777 the Purfleet magazine was hit by lightning, although only a few bricks were dislodged in the strike. This was, however, enough for the one dissenting committee member, Benjamin Wilson. He suggested that this proved that his own idea of using blunt rods, preferably with 'knobs' on the end, was superior to Franklin's 'points', as points would actually encourage 'the very mischief we mean to prevent'. The learned men of the Royal Society conducted their own experiments and disagreed, much to Wilson's fury.

This fracas had all the makings of a minor back-room scientific feud, and it would have remained so, were it not for the fact that this was the late eighteenth century and Benjamin Franklin was one of the signatories of the American Declaration of Independence, over which a war with Britain was then raging. The scientific supporters of 'points' and 'knobs' ludicrously became equated with the opposing sides in the American War of Independence. To favour a 'point' was to support the rebels fighting against their true king, whilst to prefer a 'knob' was an act of patriotic British duty. As Wilson put it, Britain was duty-bound to 'discard the invention of an enemy'.

Furthermore, the vaguely unstable King George III agreed with him. He ordered all 'points' to be removed from government buildings and replaced with 'knobs' forthwith, although, as with many of George's pronouncements, it's unclear whether the order was ever carried out. The king further attempted to force the Royal Society to reverse its committee's decision on the matter, but its brave president, Sir John Pringle, when summoned before the irate monarch, boldly stated: 'My duty, sire, as well as my inclination, would always induce me to execute your Majesty's wishes to the utmost of my power, but I cannot reverse the laws and operations of nature.' To thank him for his disarming honesty, the king promptly had him fired, both from his post at the Royal Society and in his capacity as royal physician.

Across the Atlantic, Franklin, who famously hated arguments, simply noted wryly that the king's changing of 'points' for 'knobs' was 'a matter of little importance to me. If I had a wish about it, it would be that he had rejected them altogether as ineffectual. For it is only since he thought himself and his family safe from the thunder of heaven, that he dared to use his own thunder in destroying his innocent subjects.'

A friend of Franklin's later summed up the general view in this splendidly treasonable verse:

> While you, great George, for knowledge hunt,
> And sharp conductors change for blunt,
> The nation's out of joint:
> Franklin a wiser course pursues,
> And all your thunder useless views
> By keeping to the point.

The argument – on both the shape of lightning conductors and the fate of the American people – was, of course, eventually decided in Franklin's favour.

∾

Perhaps the only way for scientists to
defeat the spin of politicians is to clearly record
their results. Odd things can happen to people
so it's vital that your work is safely on
paper, even if it costs you a goose.

∾

The Scottish Book

There are two unusual things about the Scottish Book. The first is that is has absolutely nothing to do with Scotland and the second is that, whilst it contains an awful lot of writing, it contains very few words.

The Scottish Book came about because a café owner in Lviv, or Lwów as it was back in the late 1920s and early 1930s, didn't like people writing on his tables. This was a cause of great sadness to the brilliant Polish mathematician Stefan Banach, because the ability to write in pencil on the marble tabletops of the Café Szkocka was precisely what he and his friends liked about it most.

Mathematics is often seen as a solitary occupation and, indeed, many mathematicians labour for years in splendid isolation, but this was not the preferred way of the Lwów School of Mathematics. They would meet, often every day, in the Café Szkocka, to discuss and try to solve the most pressing and complex problems in mathematics by working on them together, whilst surrounded by the noise and music of the café and engaging in bouts of heavy drinking. With minds like that of the largely self-taught Stefan Banach, who had opened up a whole new branch of mathematics (known as functional analysis), progress was rapid, but it was also messy.

Whilst writing on tables did (and still does) appeal to some mathematicians as a spontaneous way of recording new ideas and insights as they occur, it has a number of drawbacks. First, it's difficult to take your table away with you without the café owner complaining. Second, there's a real danger that the owner will clean off your important work when you finally leave. Finally, there's a reasonable chance that the owner will eventually tire of wiping away your algebra and ask you to do your mathematics and your drinking elsewhere.

Fortunately for the Lwów School, help was at hand. According to Stanislaw Ulam – one of the leading lights of the group and later a key participant in the Manhattan project to build a nuclear bomb – Banach's wife came up with a creative solution that was beyond even the genius of her husband and his illustrious group. She bought them a large notebook. The book was then handed to the grateful owner of the café who kept it with some reverence in a secret place, ceremoniously bringing it out when the Lwów School arrived and returning it to safety when they left.

And the book soon became worth protecting. Now known as 'the Scottish Book' (after the Scottish – Szkocka – café where the group met), it rapidly filled with problems and puzzles in mathematics and their proposed solutions as laid down by some of the finest minds of the era. Visitors to the café could ask to see the book and might even hazard solutions to problems written in it, for some of which the writer offered a prize, including in one case (Problem 153 set by Stanisław Mazur) a live goose. Between 1935 and 1941, over 190 problems were added to the book.

In 1941 the entries suddenly stopped. Lwów had been ceded to the Soviet Union at the beginning of the Second World War but during Operation Barbarossa (the German invasion of the USSR) it was seized by the Nazis. All universities were closed. Stefan Banach and other members of the group got by only by taking jobs as lice feeders at Rudolf Weigl's Typhus Research Institute. Weigl's work on typhus vaccine was of great interest to the Nazis and his institute required large numbers of humans to provide the blood that his lice needed to survive. It was unpleasant but, through his 'lice feeder' programme, Weigl managed to save many Polish academics from deportation to the concentration camps. Others in the Lwów School, notably many Jewish mathematicians, were not so fortunate.

During this time the Scottish Book disappeared and with it the work of this extraordinary group of mathematicians. The missing book now took on legendary status, its contents the source of rumour and its whereabouts a mystery.

Only much later, in 1958, did Professor Edward Copson of Edinburgh University receive a surprising letter from Stanislaw Ulam, then working at Los Alamos on a type of high-yield nuclear weapon that still bears his name. It begins: 'The enclosed collection of mathematical problems has its origins in a note-book which was started in Lwów, in Poland in 1935.'

Ulam had last visited Poland just before war was declared and had spoken to other group members about the notebook. He wrote to Professor Copson:

[Stanisław] Mazur in a discussion concerning such possi-bilities, suddenly said to me 'A world war may break out. What shall we do with the Scottish Book and our joint unpublished papers? You are leaving for the United States shortly – and presumably will be safe. In case of a bombard-ment of the city, I shall put all the manuscripts and the Scottish Book into a case which I shall bury in the ground.' We even decided upon a location of this secret hiding place; it was to be near the goal post of a football field outside the city.

Whether Mazur had buried the book and then dug it up after the war, none of the surviving group would say, but somehow a typed manuscript of its contents had appeared the previous year and had been sent to Ulam by one of the founders of the group. This mathematical grail now rested on Professor Copson's desk. With the problems and prizes back in the public domain, mathematicians set about them with renewed gusto. In 1972, Per Enflo finally cracked Problem 153 and, in a live television broadcast, Stanisław Mazur handed over to him the live goose he had promised for its solution in those distant, heady, pre-war days.

⁓

So whether in politics, in prison, inventing engines or splitting water, it's quite clear that science is not always fair. In particular it has not always been fair to women as quite a few stories in this book will demonstrate. Science requires not simply that you do the work, but that you have a loud enough voice to tell the world and so take the credit. As Charles Darwin's son Francis said, 'In science the credit goes to the man who convinces the world, not to the man to whom the idea first occurs.'

⁓

Singing in the rain

It was on a rare trip to New York City in the winter of 1903 that Mary Anderson came up with one of the most lucrative and commonplace inventions of the modern age. As she was a female inventor at the turn of the twentieth century, it would also be one that brought her neither fame nor fortune.

Anderson had been born on the Burton Hill Plantation in Greene County, Alabama, in 1866 at a time when the opportunities available to women were, to say the least, somewhat limited. Following the death of her father, there was very little choice but to either become an independent woman or find a husband, and quickly. Anderson chose the former. By the time she arrived in New York, aged thirty-seven, she had already become a successful property developer, owning an apartment block in Birmingham, Alabama, but what interested her that day was what was happening on the streets, not the buildings.

It was a cold New York winter, biting cold with slushy snow falling, and it was both freezing cold and wet inside the trolley-car in which she was travelling. The reason it was cold and wet *inside* was that the driver had been forced to fold down the windscreen as it kept getting covered in snow, blinding him to the road ahead. This, Anderson thought, was ludicrous. What was needed was a simple way of keeping the windscreen clear from the inside. And so she invented one – windscreen wipers. They consisted of a hand-operated spring-loaded arm, attached to a rubber blade that swept across the glass.

Mary Anderson's patent of 1904 granted her seventeen exclusive years of use for the device but it would turn out to be exactly the wrong seventeen years. During that time, motor cars remained few and far between. Many didn't have enclosed interiors or even windscreens, as early cars didn't go fast enough to require them. Despite her offering the device to various manufacturers, all remained entirely unenthusiastic; some even thought the idea simply dangerous as the wipers might 'hypnotise' the driver or otherwise distract them.

It was only as the patent expired that the motor industry took off and by then another woman inventor, Charlotte Bridgwood, had patented the first electrically-operated windscreen wiper. This too was met with almost total indifference by an automobile industry that didn't feel it needed women's help and again the device failed to become a commercial success, despite the rising number of accidents caused by poor driving visibility.

Indeed, in 1917 it would be J.R. Oishei's collision with a cyclist in heavy rain that inspired him to form the Tri-Continental Corporation that produced the first successful windscreen wipers – but then J.R. Oishei was a man.

Not even the men in the story of the windscreen wiper always got a fair hearing. The intermittent wiper was invented by Robert Kearns in 1963 as, being blind in one eye following an accident with a champagne cork, he found constant wipers an unnecessary distraction in what was for him already a tricky task. The big US motor companies soon took up his idea but notably neglected to pay him for it. Kearns, not one to take this lying down, embarked on fourteen years of litigation against the giant automobile manufacturers Ford and Chrysler, whose lawyers maintained that as the device contained no new components it was not patentable. Kearns argued that his invention was a new and non-obvious combination of parts, which it was. He was eventually awarded over $40 million.

∽

Finally, on our adventure through the realms of science we come to the trickiest and rarest aspect of all – success and fame. Being a great physicist does not automatically make you anything else besides: not a professional tennis player, not a top yodeller and certainly not a head of state. But that's not how many of those awed by your genius see it.

∽

President Einstein

The study of science produces many unusual ideas but none perhaps stranger than the commonly held one that someone who excels in the abstract reaches of theoretical physics should be ideally suited to just about any other walk of life.

In 1952, Albert Einstein became the focus of just this notion, by which time he had come to be seen as the undisputed genius of the twentieth century. His work in Europe between 1905 and 1915 led to the publication of his theories of Special and General Relativity, which, although little understood outside the physics establishment, were known to have revolutionised the subject. Following his move to the USA in 1933, the American publicity machine turned him from a legend in physics into a popular intellectual colossus.

Thrown into the wider world of politics, Einstein came into contact with politicians who, understandably, wanted to know the great man's views on virtually everything. After all, if Einstein – clearly the cleverest man alive – agreed with their policies, they must surely be right. Although naturally cautious, Einstein knew he could not simply hide from a world that now hung on to his every pronouncement. As he was a German Jew, one area of pressing interest, particularly in the light of the rise of Nazism in his homeland, was the establishment of a homeland for the Jews.

The Balfour Declaration of 1917, in which the British Foreign Secretary made the creation of a Jewish state in Palestine a policy aim, offered one potential solution. The idea was to divide the British Mandate there into two nations – one Jewish and the other Arab – yet Einstein remained publicly unsure. In a speech in 1938, with nationalism rampant in parts of Europe, he warned that the creation of a state for the Jews might reduce them to petty nationalism too.

However, by the end of the war that had visited the Holocaust on his people, he felt able to write that the creation of a Jewish homeland might at least go some way to redress the balance of history, although the idea of separating Jews and Arabs, possibly by force, into two nations still greatly disturbed him. And with that the great physicist hoped to return to something he really could make a difference in – physics.

The independent Jewish homeland of Israel did finally come into existence on 14 May 1948, with Chaim Weizmann (see page 81) as its first president. When Weizmann died four years later, the question arose as to who should succeed him. One of the political founders of Israel seemed the most likely choice for this highly political role, but a newspaper editor made a different suggestion, which reached the ears of Prime Minister David Ben-Gurion: why not have the most famous and eminent Jew alive, Albert Einstein? Liking the idea, Ben-Gurion duly dispatched a telegram to his ambassador in the US, Abba Eban, which read: PLEASE FIND OUT IMMEDIATELY WHETHER EINSTEIN WOULD ACCEPT THE ELECTION (BY PARLIAMENT) TO BE ISRAELI PRESIDENT.

In Princeton, New Jersey, where Einstein, then seventy-three, lived and worked, news had already reached him that an unusual offer was coming his way, thanks to the *New York Times*, which had picked up the story in Israel and wanted to know his reply. To say this was something of a surprise would be an understatement. In the first instance, Einstein wasn't Israeli, but held joint Swiss and US citizenship. Second, he was, as far as he could remember, a physicist, not a politician. This was, in essence, what he told the Israeli ambassador when he rang him, pointing out that whilst he knew a little 'of nature', politics was not his *métier*.

There is some confusion as to what happened next but either David Ben-Gurion refused to accept Einstein's refusal or the ambassador asked for a more formal written reply to satisfy the newspapers, which were jolly excited about the idea of 'President Einstein'. So on the evening of 17 November 1952, Albert Einstein took receipt of the official telegram inviting him to be president of Israel, before writing the following reply:

I am deeply moved by the offer from our State of Israel

[to serve as President], and at once saddened and ashamed that I cannot accept it. All my life I have dealt with objective matters, hence I lack both the natural aptitude and the experience to deal properly with people and to exercise official functions. For these reasons alone I should be unsuited to fulfill the duties of that high office, even if advancing age was not making increasing inroads on my strength. I am the more distressed over these circumstances because my relationship to the Jewish people has become my strongest human bond, ever since I became fully aware of our precarious situation among the nations of the world.

Einstein had made his first and last foray into political life. The glory days of Special and General Relativity may have been long behind him, but he was not yet either old enough or foolish enough to swap the modest peace of Princeton for a presidential palace.

2

Physics, Football and Fear

(In which we meet a professional footballer,
a historian, an excited Frenchman and
a very cross German.)

The laws of physics are the decrees of fate.

Alfred North Whitehead,
Science and the Modern World (1926)

Physics is a huge field. Indeed, Ernest Rutherford said that all science was 'either physics or stamp collecting', so you might expect physicists to be drawn from a wide background. This is A Good Thing as it means that even the most unlikely candidates stand a chance. Even professional footballers.

⌒∽

A physicist, distracted

Absent-minded professors (see page 7) are an enduring, perhaps even an endearing, image in science but their distraction is rarely more than a source of amusement or annoyance for those around them. In one case, however, it helped to stop one great physicist from taking a career path that would have changed our view of the modern world.

The Bohr brothers were talented – everyone knew that. Harald Bohr, the younger of the two, was seen as particularly gifted. In 1904, aged only seventeen, he enrolled at Copenhagen University, receiving his doctorate in mathematics at just twenty-two. This would be impressive enough, were it not for the fact that this was the second string to his bow, for Harald's first love was football. As in mathematics, Harald was brilliant at this too, playing half-back for the leading Danish club, Akademisk Boldklub (usually shortened to AB), having made his debut the year before he went up to university. So good indeed was his performance at AB that he was selected to play for his national side at the 1908 Olympic Games in London – the first time football had been designated an Olympic sport. Denmark's opening match in this tournament also marked their first ever official international (if we exclude the unofficial intercalated games of 1906).

It would be fair to say that Harald and Denmark's performance in those games was exceptional. In that first ever international game, Denmark beat the French 'B' team 9–0, Harald scoring two of the goals. In the semi-final, also against France, the result was even more resounding, a record 17–1 victory. Only the final proved a real match for the Danes and they lost 2–0 to Great Britain. When Harald publicly defended his doctorate just two years later, he enjoyed one of the largest audiences ever seen for such a rarefied mathematical debate, although the room was not filled with mathematicians. Instead, hundreds of football fans had gathered to meet this famous Olympic silver medallist.

Not surprisingly the limelight in these early years fell very much on Harald, but it was his older brother who would really find football life-changing. Niels Bohr also loved the game and he too signed to AB, playing alongside his brother in some matches in the 1905 season. Niels was not the exceptional sporting talent that his brother had proved to be, however. He played in goal, and not usually for the first team as, despite his obvious ability, he had an unfortunate habit of becoming distracted.

This tendency had been most noticeable during a game against the German team Mittweida when a German striker had hit a long ball forward. His AB teammates looked to Niels to save the ball, but to their dismay Niels was not looking at the ball at all. He was intently studying one of his goalposts on which he'd begun scratching some calculations. Of the two surviving accounts of the match, one claims that the ball dribbled past Bohr and into the net, whilst the other claims that a vigorous shout from the crowd awoke Niels from his daydream and he saved the goal. After the match, Niels apologised to his team, saying that a mathematical problem had suddenly come to him and he had found it necessary to make some notes on the spur of the moment. Either way it was not deemed a suitable performance for a premier goalkeeper and after the 1905 season Niels was not asked to play in the first team again.

All of which is fortunate for the world of physics. Niels Bohr, denied the fame of a sports star, went on to become one of the most celebrated figures in modern physics, a founder of quantum theory and a Nobel laureate. His brother Harald also achieved academic fame. Having hung up his boots after one further international (in which Denmark beat an amateur England side), he became a leading mathematician, founding the field of 'almost periodic functions'. When asked about his big brother's brush with sports fame he later commented: 'Yes, Niels was quite good; but he was too slow in coming out.'

ᔿ

Having escaped the First XI and made it into academe, every physicist hopes, perhaps, for enlightenment – that moment when the clouds part and the truth becomes dazzlingly clear, in this case with life-saving consequences.

ᔿ

Enlightenment

It is easy to forget that during the early stages of the Industrial Revolution the basic form of interior lighting hadn't changed for several thousand years. In the dark hours and dark places, those who could afford it would light a candle, expensive beeswax for choice, animal tallow if necessary. For those who could not afford candles, simple oil lamps made from a wick in a dish of oil had to make do, despite their dim, sooty, yellow light. None of this made working indoors or at night practical and when it came to certain lights – say, lighthouses – it was simply dangerous.

Until the 1780s a lighthouse was really little more than a bonfire on a podium but that was all about to change thanks to a Swiss eccentric who would spend his later years collecting bones and coffin fragments from graveyards in search of the Elixir of Youth. In 1780, however, François-Pierre-Aimé Argand, a pupil of Antoine-Laurent de Lavoisier (see page 11), was still young and full of good ideas.

It is uncertain how Argand came upon his big idea, as inventors sometimes like to elaborate later on their moments of enlightenment. According to his brother, the two men were having dinner in a gloomy room when somehow Aimé managed to break a glass flask. When he briefly held the neck of this over the oil lamp, he noticed instantly how the glass funnel made the flame steady and grow in brightness. His brother put it more poetically: 'Immediately it rose with brilliance. My brother started from his seat in ecstasy, rushed upon me with a transport of joy and embraced me with rapture.'

He doesn't mention whether the two of them had been drinking but, rapturous embrace or not, Argand had conceived of a whole new type of lamp. In fact, the glass funnel or chimney would form only one of three crucial parts to what would become known as the Argand lamp. Argand also replaced the thick solid wick with a hollow one, allowing oxygen to rise up the inside of the wick. This combined with the glass chimney to steady the flame and increase the draw of air from below. Together with a mechanism for raising and lowering the wick to achieve an optimum length, it made for the greatest breakthrough in lighting in four millennia. An Argand lamp was as bright as seven candles and burnt its oil, ideally spermaceti oil from a sperm whale, efficiently without sooting up. This was good news all round, unless you were a sperm whale, of course.

Argand decided to move to England where he could get a patent as well as access to flint glass manufacturers who could make glass chimneys that wouldn't shatter in the heat of the flame. There he could also escape the crowings of Antoine-Arnoult Quinquet, to whom he had shown his invention in France. Quinquet had promptly stolen the idea and patented it; indeed, this type of lamp is still known to the French as a *quinquet*. To ram the point home, the plagiarising Gallic inventor took to wearing a hat on which he had painted: 'I am Quinquet, the inventor of quinquets' – which he wasn't. Argand had at one point challenged Quinquet's business partner Lange to a duel over the issue but, perhaps thankfully for both of them, Lange had declined.

In England, Argand had more luck and was granted a patent. He was fortunate too in meeting a number of early industrialists, including the 'Lunaticks' James Watt and his future business partner Matthew Boulton (see page 20), all of whom were interested in providing high-intensity interior lighting that would enable people to work after dark, as well as in enclosed murky spaces such as those 'dark satanic mills' that were then becoming all the rage.

Here his work came to the attention of the Stevenson dynasty, the family of Scottish engineers who had dedicated themselves to the building and improvement of lighthouses. Robert Stevenson had been the first to suggest that lighthouses have three keepers instead of the usual two, after an incident on the Smalls Lighthouse when one keeper died and the other kept his putrefying body in a box lashed to the lantern rail for a month for fear of being accused of his murder. Stevenson was also keen to experiment with lenses, reflectors and rotating mechanisms that could make the light 'flash', his concept being that each light could have a unique flashing pattern so that sailors would know not only that there was a lighthouse near by but which one it was.

But it was light that Stevenson most needed and in Argand's lamp he saw the means of producing a beam that was very bright, needed little trimming and didn't soot up the lantern housing. In 1789 the first Argand lamp shone out from a British light-house and with it was born the era of modern illumination.

❧

Physics can be a surprisingly practical and varied career. Indeed, it is such a broad church that you don't even have to be a physicist to do it. In fact, seeing a problem from the outside can be just what's needed when looking for a solution. Nor does it even need to be done by outsiders who fancy themselves as physicists. Sometimes the subject and the hand of chance choose you.

❧

The late Mrs Morse

Samuel Finley Breese Morse did not invent the telegraph, which isn't all that surprising as he was, by trade, a painter. Yet the telegraph and the famous code that it transmitted are inextric-ably linked to his name, thanks to a family tragedy and a dull sea crossing.

Morse had been born in 1791 into a devout Calvinist family in Charlestown, Massachusetts, and had studied religious philoso-phy at Yale College before setting himself up as a painter, specialising in historical scenes. His work was good enough to attract the attention of the celebrated US artist Washington Allston who took the young Morse with him to England on the first of his many trips across the Atlantic. In England and continental Europe, Morse honed his skills, whilst back in the USA his reputation grew and greater commissions awaited, including one that would change his and all of our lives, for ever.

In 1825 the city of New York asked Morse to paint the Marquis de Lafayette, the fêted Revolutionary War general who was then in Washington as the 'National Guest' of President James Monroe. Lafayette and Morse got on well and on 10 February Morse wrote home to his wife Lucretia, telling her of his convivial life in the capital. The next day, during one sitting with the marquis, a horse messenger arrived with an urgent letter for Morse from his father. It contained just four hard-hitting words: 'Your Wife is Dead.'

Morse, distraught, instantly set off for the family home in New Haven but by the time he arrived his wife had already been buried. Far from home, and with no rapid communication, he had been writing to a woman who was already three days dead and who, because of the distance, had died alone, without the comfort of his presence, following the birth of their third child. It was this tragedy that laid the foundations for a remarkable change in Morse's career.

Morse's great idea did not bear fruit immediately. It was not until seven years later, on an interminable journey across the Atlantic from Europe aboard the *Sully*, that a conversation on deck between the scientist Charles T. Jackson, Morse and others led to his breakthrough. Jackson had been demonstrating to his fellow passengers a device he had purchased in Europe – an electromagnet – and it occurred to Morse that this might form the basis of a single-wire telegraph. He had already seen a mechanical semaphore telegraph in France but realised it was too slow for mass communication. Electricity looked much more promising or, as he put it, 'the lightning would serve us better'.

By this date there were other telegraphs in operation.

Georges-Louis Le Sage had built his 'frictional electric tele-graph' as early as 1774 and the Englishman Peter Barlow had proposed a device in 1824. In the US, Harrison Gray Dyar and his brother Joseph had also demonstrated a frictional telegraph in 1826, something Morse probably knew of and some of whose ideas he may have 'borrowed', as one of Harrison's friends was his brother-in-law. These systems, however, had a very limited range as the signal faded when transmitted over long wires, due to resistance and current leakage, and so the message was soon lost.

Morse was a painter, not a scientist, and his initial attempts to construct his own telegraph suffered from one substantial drawback. They didn't work. What Morse needed was expert help. He found this in the form of three men: Leonard Gale, a professor of chemistry at New York University; Joseph Henry, the head of the Smithsonian Institution; and Alfred Vail, a talented electrical engineer. Whilst Vail improved the relays Morse had designed, Henry demonstrated how the circuit necessary for the single-wire telegraph could be made using the earth to complete it. In addition, he developed a thick insulating rubber covering to protect the wire and the glass insulators that attached it to the telegraph poles (which had been a suggestion of another friend, Ezra Cornell). Leonard Gale then set to work on Morse's slightly clumsy recording system, which he replaced with a clock-driven, pen-and-ink recorder.

Thanks to this group effort, the modern telegraph slowly came into existence but one problem still remained: the signal faded over distance. It was Henry again who came to the rescue, designing battery-operated relays that could be placed every ten miles to boost the signal. Now the telegraph could theoretically reach anywhere in the country.

With the telegraph fully functional, it was time to head for Washington to secure state funding. Predictably, this was not forthcoming. Morse travelled to Europe to look for better luck, only to discover that his British rivals William Cooke and Charles Wheatstone (see page 171), who had started work after him, had already launched a commercial telegraph service, albeit using a different system.

Despite this, Morse remained undaunted and, following further improvements, he returned to Washington, to demonstrate his telegraph in the committee rooms of Congress. This time the congressmen were more impressed and the substantial sum of $3,000 was secured for an experimental 38-mile telegraph between Washington DC and Baltimore. It was along this line, on 24 May 1844, that Morse sent his famous message celebrating the official opening of the line, taken from the Biblical book of Numbers: 'What hath God wrought.'

The following year the Magnetic Telegraph Company was founded to spread the telegraph across the expanding USA, but it would not be all plain sailing for Morse. Whilst honours followed him in Europe, his patent was not only frequently contested but more often simply ignored, and the US government failed to grant him any official recognition. Indeed, it was a consortium of European countries together with Russia and Turkey that eventually clubbed together to make Morse an award of 400,000 French francs for his work. They had, in 1851, adopted the Morse telegraphic apparatus as the European standard for telegraphy – with the notable exception of Great Britain, which chose to use its own system.

Finally, the year before his death, Morse received some little recognition in his home country with the erecting of a small bronze in Central Park, New York City. He died in 1872 aged eighty, still fighting to be universally recognised as the inventor of the telegraph. For such a group effort the claim was perhaps a shade rich, but in the end Morse got his way and his telegraph, and more importantly the code sent down it, are known simply as 'Morse'.

∽

Great physicists can think outside the box. They
are creators, working with new ideas and new
materials, searching for new ways of seeing.
For them the whole world is an experiment and
they can find their apparatus in the most
unlikely of places.

∽

Stephen Gray's electrical schoolboys

Stephen Gray's name is not one that today has any real currency
(if those of you who already know about him will forgive the
pun). This is a great shame as it is unusual for the British to
forget one of their scientific pioneers, and Gray, both in his
brilliant insight and his magnificent demonstrations, deserves a
place up with the best of them.

Stephen Gray (who was baptised in 1666) was not born into
the sort of money that allowed gentlemen of the period to pursue
a life in science. Nevertheless, thanks to his brother, who was
sometime mayor of Canterbury, he was able to make contact
with some of the greatest scientific figures of his day, prompting
in him a passion for natural curiosities. Armed only with some
copies of the Royal Society's journal *Philosophical Transactions*
and whatever materials he had to hand, he embarked on a career
of discovery. He began by studying small organisms in the various
liquids he found around him, including saliva, urine, brandy,
beer and vinegar (see page 269), developing in the process the
first 'poor man's microscope', constructed by placing a drop of
water over a small hole in a brass plate. From here he went on
to providing the first Astronomer Royal, John Flamsteed, with
detailed astronomical observations, even being asked to assist

in the setting up of an observatory at Trinity College, Cambridge, by the then Lucasian Professor of Mathematics, Roger Cotes.

What most interested Stephen Gray was electricity. The early eighteenth century was the first great era of electrical discovery. Apparatus to create static charge was regularly demonstrated at the Royal Society and in the homes of learned members such as Sir Hans Sloane, but no one could produce a theory to explain exactly what electricity was or how it acted. By 1706, Gray had managed to give up labouring as a dyer, a job that had crippled his health, and get work as an assistant at the Royal Society, where he had access to the sort of equipment he could never have previously afforded. At last he could set his mind to solving the mystery of electricity.

By 1718, however, his experiments looked close to coming to an end, as he was destitute. It appears that his scientific work at the Royal Society was probably unpaid, other than in the provision of accommodation, and much of his previous work with the great names of the day had been undertaken in his own time and wholly at his own expense. His work was rescued only by the intervention of his old friends Sir Hans Sloane and John Flamsteed. They successfully petitioned the Prince of Wales (the future George II) to nominate Gray for admission to the Charterhouse, a charitable institution that ran a school and a home for destitute gentlemen. When Stephen Gray arrived at his new lodgings, at least no longer in fear of the workhouse, he was armed with one of the Royal Society's glass tube friction generators.

The glass tube generator was one of the most advanced pieces of electrical equipment of the day, utilising friction to create a static electrical charge. Gray immediately set it up in his new rooms. In doing so he noticed that the cork in the end of the tube, which kept out dust and moisture, could itself attract small articles when the tube was 'charged', implying that the 'electrical virtue', as he put it, could be transferred to another object.

Wondering over what distance this would still work, he placed a wooden spill in the cork and charged the tube, discovering that the charge now extended to the end of the wooden stick. Soon Gray's room was a spider's web of cords and cables attached to the end of the tube. In his experiments he noted how some materials, such as hemp cord, carried the charge but others, such as silk, would not. He also noted how, when the electrical virtue was allowed to touch the ground, it seemed to disappear.

By this time Gray needed more room. He went to visit the Reverend Granville Wheeler in his old home county of Kent where the two constructed elaborate looms of thread, one over 800 feet long, down which the electrical virtue could be transmitted. In the process the pair discovered that by suspending the cord on silk threads they could prevent the charge seeping away to the earth.

These were huge breakthroughs in the understanding of electricity. Although he did not always fully understand the reasons behind all of his experimental results, Gray had demonstrated the action of an earth on an electrical field and the operation of electricity along a conductor, along with its failure to travel down an insulator. The terms 'insulator' and 'conductor' would later be coined by Gray's boss at the Royal Society, Jean Desaguliers (see page 15).

What Gray really needed was a spectacular demonstration to convince the grand gentlemen of the Royal Society of his discoveries. This led to his devising his most famous experiment – the flying boy. Charterhouse, it will be remembered, was both a refuge for distressed gentlemen and a boys' school, so Gray availed himself of one of the boys for his first great demonstration of electrical conductance. The unfortunate child was first laid down and then hoisted horizontally into the air, supported around the middle by a series of insulating silk cords. The glass tube friction generator was then charged and touched against the boy's foot. When he reached out with a pointed finger towards a small tray of brass flakes, they magically twitched and twisted as the boy's finger approached. For added effect Gray created a 'series' of flying boys, connected by iron rods, to demonstrate the action of electricity over a longer distance.

It was, even for its day, an unusual experimental set-up, but it demonstrated for the first time the role of conductors and insulators, and suggested that electricity was a surface effect that 'flowed' along objects attached to a generator. At last Gray began to achieve some recognition. In 1731 he was awarded the first ever Copley medal by the Royal Society, receiving a second medal the following year. In that year he also finally became a member of the Society himself, an honour long denied him due to the bitter feud between Sir Isaac Newton (see page 24) and Gray's friend John Flamsteed, which prevented him from being admitted in Newton's lifetime.

Stephen Gray, never the gentleman scientist but arguably the father of electrical communication, died on 17 February 1736, still destitute, and was buried in an unmarked pauper's grave. Disgracefully, he has no monument.

But if physicists can call the whole world
their laboratory, they can't always choose which
bit of it they get to work in. Accident and fate
play a part in every life, although this
never puts a good physicist off . . .

Chadwick's toothpaste

Whilst James Chadwick is best known today as the discoverer of the neutron, his astonishing career in physics was only made possible thanks to a series of unfortunate incidents.

Chadwick came from humble beginnings, the son of a cotton spinner living near Macclesfield, but his brilliance at mathematics was noted at the Manchester Central Grammar School and he was encouraged to apply to Manchester University, to which he received a scholarship when only sixteen.

Painfully shy, Chadwick turned up to enrol, unsure about where he was or what he was meant to do, other than sign up for a degree in mathematics. Due to his extraordinary reticence, he sat down with the wrong interviewer but lacked the courage to admit his mistake and move on. As this interviewer was recruiting for the physics course, Chadwick became a physicist.

The young scientist soon came to the notice of Ernest Rutherford, who had won the Nobel prize for his contribution to the new field of nuclear physics in 1908 and who encouraged the impoverished Chadwick to take a scholarship to study with Hans Geiger (the inventor of the Geiger counter) in Berlin. Chadwick agreed and in Berlin met many of the stars of the new age of nuclear physics, including Lise Meitner (see page 209), Albert Einstein and Otto Hahn. Unfortunately he was still in Berlin at the outset of the First World War.

When war was declared, Geiger gave Chadwick money in case he needed to leave the country. Chadwick immediately took this to the Cook's Tours office in Berlin where he hoped to get a ticket to Holland and thence to England. In the blizzard of troop movements taking place all over Europe, Cook's were not sure whether this was a good idea and recommended that he wait until things calmed down, then leave via neutral Switzerland instead. This proved a mistake. Two days later Chadwick was arrested, nominally for making subversive remarks but in fact for simply being an enemy alien. He would spend the four years of the war not in England, Holland or Switzerland, but in the requisitioned Ruhleben racecourse stables, near Spandau, which were converted to hold civilian prisoners.

Life in Ruhleben, whose name rather appropriately means 'Life of Peace', was quiet but extremely hard. Chadwick's constitution would in fact be wrecked by the experience, but it was not without its diversions. Various 'clubs' were set up by the prisoners, including a 'science circle', which received some basic equipment and books from friendly German former colleagues such as Meitner and Max Planck (see page 59). With the most primitive and hand-made equipment, Chadwick managed to set up a laboratory, but materials to study, particularly nuclear ones, proved – as one might expect in the circumstances – hard to come by.

Eventually he discovered that a German toothpaste (see page 130) was advertised as radioactive – those were the days when many still considered radioactivity to be a miracle cure for just about anything – and he persuaded the guards to give him regular deliveries. Through stockpiling this substance, he eventually acquired enough to study it with a home-made electroscope, noting that the toothpaste behaved like no other radioactive substance then known.

Through his work he also met the young Englishman Charles Ellis, an engineering cadet who had been trapped in Germany whilst on holiday, and he persuaded him to turn his attentions from engineering to physics. Ellis would later be instrumental in the discovery of the neutrino.

Chadwick was finally released in 1918, at the end of the war, Ruhleben having at least saved him from the fate of so many young physicists who had died at the front. He returned to England to continue what would become an illustrious career in physics. This cotton spinner's son would go on to win a Nobel prize and receive a knighthood, neither of which would have been possible were it not for a misunderstanding at enrolment and some bad travel advice.

∽

Whilst the world of physics may, at least in the
past, have been full of painters and electrified
schoolboys, there was still the 'establishment' to
deal with. Physics is a sober and serious pursuit
and not open to just anyone. Not without
an invitation.

∽

De Broglie catches a wave

Occasionally even historians can make a small contribution to
science, although to be fair the de Broglie family were always
more the sort whom history happened to rather than those who
simply studied it. The young Louis-Victor Pierre Raymond, later
Duc de Broglie, was a member of the old French aristocracy,
one of whose ancestors had been guillotined in the Revolution,
so history ran very much in his veins. So, like many of his class,
he was expected to study the subject before taking up a career
in the military or possibly the diplomatic corps.

Although de Broglie read history at the Sorbonne, he was
always more interested in his older brother's work as a scientist
and, to the frustration of his tutors, he spent most of his time
studying that instead. Once he had graduated, the outbreak of
the First World War gave de Broglie a chance to take a more
practical interest in science and, having joined the army, he
volunteered for the radio communication service based at the
Eiffel Tower. Here he discovered that it was not history or even
the practical, experimental science of his brother that interested
him, but rather theoretical physics. When peace came, he
returned to academia a changed man.

It was perhaps not unreasonable that the professors of physics of the day (it was now 1924) might take a sceptical view of this aristocratic historian now treading on their toes. The title he had given his doctoral thesis was, after all, rather grand: 'Research on Quantum Theory'. What it contained was also rather odd.

The world of physics had recently been rocked by two very simple equations. The first, put forward by Albert Einstein (see page 36), stated that energy equalled mass times the speed of light squared ($E=mc^2$). The second had been postulated by Max Planck (see page 278) in 1900: that energy also equalled frequency times a tiny number (h) known as the Planck Constant ($E=hv$). These were two different equations, useful in two different ways: on that everyone was generally agreed.

To those reading de Broglie's thesis, however, what he concluded from these equations was a shade more alarming. De Broglie, not trained from early years as a scientist but nonetheless a brilliant theoretician, noted that if $E=mc^2$ and $E=hv$, then surely all matter must behave like a wave. Everything with a mass has energy (as Einstein had stated), energy implies frequency (as Planck had stated), and frequency obviously implies a wave, so particles in motion must behave like waves.

To the examiners this was clearly just the sort of nonsensical physics you might expect from a historian. Particles were discrete lumps of stuff that behaved like, well, particles, and waves were waves – like sound and light. But nagging at the back of their minds remained one thought. Einstein and Planck had already turned their world upside down. What if de Broglie was right and he was flipping them round again? As none of the examiners could work it out, the only answer was to send the thesis to the great Einstein and, rather apologetically, ask whether the enclosed work was genius or gibberish.

And so they, and de Broglie, waited. Eventually Einstein wrote back: 'I believe it is a first feeble ray of light on this worst of our physics enigmas.'

Whilst it was not perhaps the ringing endorsement that the supervisor had hoped for, Einstein wasn't a man to get easily overexcited. Crucially, he thought the work was sound: de Broglie was right and, as he put it: 'any moving particle or object had an associated wave'. De Broglie was immediately awarded his doctorate.

∽

Not only do physicists need to get
in, they need to get their ideas in first.

∽

Lenard rays

X-rays were, of course, discovered by Wilhelm Röntgen, but that doesn't mean he was necessarily the first to notice them. On the fateful day in November 1895 when Röntgen made his breakthrough, he was experimenting with someone else's equipment, in particular a device invented by the German physicist Philipp Lenard.

Lenard had himself been interested in experimenting with the invention of English physicist William Crookes, the 'Crookes tube', in which cathode rays had first been discovered. Lenard found it difficult to study cathode rays in the tube – a partially evacuated and sealed glass cylinder. To overcome this he had managed to insert a 'window' in the tube, which consisted of a small square of aluminium, thick enough to prevent the tube from collapsing but, crucially, thin enough for the cathode rays to pass out of the tube and into the room.

It was whilst Röntgen was setting up one of these 'Lenard tubes' that he became aware of something odd. Cathode rays were known to be quickly dispersed in air. He observed, however, that a detecting screen lying on a table on the other side of the laboratory, far outside the range of the cathode rays coming from his tube, was fluorescing. Some other sort of ray was clearly leaving the tube. Röntgen immediately set to work exploring the properties of the ray, discovering along the way that it could pass apparently unhindered through some solid substances. Most importantly he realised that the rays passed through flesh but were absorbed by bone. A photographic plate of a part of a living body exposed to X-rays showed the bones inside. This would set the stage for a medical revolution.

On New Year's Day 1896, Röntgen put into envelopes several copies of his paper on X-rays, as he had decided to call them, and a radiograph of his wife's hand (complete with wedding ring), and sent them to the leading scientists of the day, including Henri Poincaré (see page 264) and Lord Kelvin. He also sent a copy to Austrian physicist Franz Exner with whom he had worked some years earlier. Furthermore he mentioned the picture to his father who happened to edit the Austrian newspaper *Neue Freie Presse* in Vienna. The following week the story was headline news in Vienna and from there was quickly picked up by all the world's press.

The instant fame now accorded to Röntgen somewhat surprised him. In just a year, 1,044 papers would appear on the new 'miracle' ray, and scientists and politicians from across the globe asked to visit his laboratory. He was offered a title by the German state and honoured with membership of the world's most exclusive scientific societies. Then in 1901 he was awarded the first Nobel prize for physics.

It was perhaps this last plaudit that pushed Philipp Lenard over the edge. Lenard had been incensed by Röntgen's discovery, not least because he had seen similar results to Röntgen. Vitally, however, he had thought them just another type of cathode ray and had not experimented further. Röntgen had, but he had done it with one of Lenard's tubes and this, Lenard believed, gave *him* a right to be called the discoverer of X-rays.

For a while it looked as if Lenard might get his way and the rays were initially referred to as 'Lenard-Röntgen rays', although Lenard still insisted he should have sole billing. When both names were put forward for the Nobel prize, the committee decided that providing the equipment for an experiment was not the same as making a discovery with it, so they awarded the prize to Röntgen alone.

To say Lenard was apoplectic would be something of an understatement. At every occasion he attempted to discredit Röntgen, claiming that he was the 'mother' of X-rays and that Röntgen was merely the 'midwife'. In lectures when mentioning X-rays he would turn to his students and sternly ask: 'And who did this first?' The only acceptable answer was: 'You, Herr Professor.' Röntgen, who had hardly profited from the discovery, not even having patented it, was utterly bemused.

Whilst this seems on the surface like a silly scientific spat, it planted the seeds of something much worse. Lenard, for all the good science he did in his early years (winning a Nobel prize himself in 1905), became deeply embittered, believing the whole scientific community was conspiring against him. He also began claiming that British physicist J.J. Thomson, the discoverer of the electron, had stolen that idea from him too, and he denounced what he called the materialism and egotism of British physics as alien to German culture.

From 1919, Lenard began espousing a 'new physics', which he called 'German physics' and which he hoped would be untainted by the 'Jewish physics of men like Einstein' (see page 37), who had correctly explained some of Lenard's own results when he could not (this being the work that gained Einstein his Nobel prize).

Convinced that he was surrounded by charlatans who had stolen his glory, and by Jewish conspirators who were trying to replace solid science with abstract and obscure mathematics, Lenard was a natural ally for the rising Nazi Party. Under Hitler he would become 'Chief of Aryan Physics' and the author of the four-volume *Deutsche Physik*, which denounced the 'Jewish Fraud' of relativity and Röntgen for doing 'Jewish physics', which was both ludicrous and odd, as Röntgen was not Jewish.

Out of touch with the new direction that physics had taken in the twentieth century, and now a mere mouthpiece of the Nazi propaganda machine, Lenard would spend his last years in bitter isolation, his own brilliant work, for which he could rightly take credit, and his own Nobel prize all but forgotten.

❧

Even theoretical physicists can sometimes find themselves in danger, even without dodgy advice from their travel agents. All that they need is something to mark them out as special. And nothing marks you out quite like a Nobel prize.

❧

All that glisters

In April 1940, German forces invaded Denmark, placing the celebrated physicist Niels Bohr (see page 43) in something of a quandary. There was of course the danger of his work on nuclear theory falling into Nazi hands as well as the safety of his staff at the Institute of Theoretical Physics in Copenhagen to consider. But there was also the problem of the Nobel medals.

The medals awarded with the Nobel prize were, up until 1980, made of solid 23-carat gold and so had a considerable value. More than that, their whereabouts might reveal where someone's true sympathies lay. And that was Bohr's difficulty. His own Nobel medal was not an issue – he'd already auctioned it off on 12 March 1940 in support of the Fund for Finnish Relief.

However, there were two other medals still in his possession. One belonged to the physicist James Franck, who had fled Germany shortly after Hitler's rise to power, leaving his medal for safe keeping with Bohr. The other belonged to another physicist, Max von Laue, who even then was still in Germany, continuing to teach the proscribed 'Jewish physics' of Albert Einstein (see page 37).

Both medals placed Bohr in an awkward situation. If the Institute were searched, which it might be at any moment, the medals might be found and confiscated, which would obviously upset the owners. More worryingly, the presence of the medals in Bohr's care might indicate to the German authorities that von Laue was secretly in favour of Bohr's institute, which had sheltered many Jewish scientists. Even the ownership of a Nobel was now regarded with suspicion in Germany since Hitler had decreed that Germans could not receive them.

Bohr went to see George de Hevesy who also worked at the Institute and would also later become a Nobel laureate. He suggested burying the medals, which would be simple and probably effective, but, according to de Hevesy's later account, Bohr was still anxious that they would be found. So he proposed something more fundamental: he would dissolve them.

Dissolving gold is no mean feat as the metal is highly unreactive but de Hevesy managed it using aqua regia – a solution of nitric and concentrated hydrochloric acids. Having dissolved the medals, which were presumably milled first to speed up the process, the Nobel liquid was poured into two bottles and placed on a shelf in the laboratory. And there they waited. The Institute was later searched but the bottles of orange liquid went unnoticed. Bohr later himself fled first to Sweden and thence to England. Still the bottles remained on the shelf.

Indeed, the apparently dull bottles remained there for the whole war. With Germany defeated and the physicists returned to the Institute, it now remained only to explain to James Franck and Max von Laue what had happened to their medals. Fortunately de Hevesy was more than capable of reversing the process. The gold was removed from the aqua regia, albeit not in medal form. Niels Bohr then arranged for the recovered gold to be sent back to the Royal Swedish Academy of Sciences, which recoined the medals for their grateful recipients.

∽

Physicists can be drawn from the
most unlikely of backgrounds to perform the
most unlikely of experiments in the most
unlikely of places for the most glittering, if
dangerous, of rewards. However, getting those
rewards requires an amazing result.
Thankfully, in physics, as in all other walks of
life, this involves not just genius, but luck.

∽

Otto Stern's passive smoking

The physics laboratories of the 1920s could be different places to laboratories today. Nowhere was this more immediately apparent than in the prevalence of smoking at work, something that would now almost always be banned. Yet without one scientist's love of cigars, the age of quantum mechanics might never have been ushered in.

One of the fundamental complications with the model of quantum physics proposed by former goalkeeper Niels Bohr (see page 43) and others was that it seemed to offer experimental physicists very little to get their teeth into. Almost none of it appeared experimentally provable (or unprovable) and therefore many of its opponents could, with some justification, claim that it was just a pretty piece of mathematics. That was until Einstein's first pupil, Otto Stern, took to cheap cigars.

Stern was a brilliant practical physicist who had a particular interest in space quantisation. In quantum theory, 'space quantisation' described how the plane of an orbiting electron in an atom could have only a certain number of orientations, so rather than having a continuous range of angles it would be forced to be in one plane or another. For most scientists, this was just a formula for explaining away a piece of mathematics; indeed, many believed it was no more than a way of imagining the theory, but Stern, ever the optimist, wondered whether he might be able to prove it experimentally.

Although it was not a popular idea with his fellow scientists, Stern found one ally in Walther Gerlach. Together they designed and built an experiment in which a furnace was used to produce a beam of silver atoms, which were then aligned through two small slits and sent past a large magnet. Classical theory suggested that the collector plate at the end of the beam would show a spread of silver atoms as electrons orbiting in different random orientations, which would mean that the atoms would be deflected differently by the magnet. Quantum theory suggested something of another nature altogether. It theorised that the atoms would be deflected discretely, either up or down, depending on the 'spin state' of each.

It was a brilliantly simply experiment held back only by the fact that, when they tried it, it didn't seem to work. So tenuous was the thin film of silver atoms, and so close would the two spots be to one another, if the theory was correct, that when Stern and Gerlach examined the plate they could initially see nothing. After a time its surface began to change. As Stern himself recorded: 'After venting to release the vacuum, Gerlach removed the detector flange. But he could see no trace of the silver atom beam and handed the flange to me. With Gerlach looking over my shoulder as I peered closely at the plate, we were surprised to see gradually emerge the trace of a beam.'

It was a while before Stern realised what was happening. Working in a poorly funded lab in 1920s Germany, he couldn't afford good-quality cigars and so was forced to smoke cheap ones that used a large quantity of sulphur to help the low-grade tobacco burn more evenly. As he stood puffing his usual cigar, peering at the plate, he was unwittingly breathing out sulphur compounds, which were combining with the previously invisible traces of silver on the plate to form black silver sulphide – almost like developing a photograph.

It was still early days and much further refining of the experiment was needed, as well as an injection of cash from an unlikely source – Henry Goldman, of the banking firm Goldman Sachs. After nearly a year when little progress seemed to be made, there was even talk of giving up the experiment, but again fate intervened when a train strike gave Gerlach an extra day at a loose end to go over his figures. Running the experiment once more, he achieved a definitive separation and could write to Stern, then at the University of Rostock: 'Bohr is right after all.' Thanks to a cheap cigar, quantum physics could come out of the realm of theory and into its own strange reality.

⤝∂

Finally in this brief excursion through the
annals of physics, we come to humour. Being
funny is not a requirement in the subject, but it
helps. It might be a little oblique, but when
you're dealing with something as mind-
numbing as the origins of the universe,
a little joke can go a long way.

⤝∂

Alpher, Bethe and Gamow

One of the most famous papers in the history of cosmology
owes its byline to a joke.

The Alpher–Bethe–Gamow paper, published in *The Physical
Review* in 1948, deals with the tricky problem of how matter
was created at the Big Bang, arguing that progressively heavier
atoms were formed by the capture of neutrons. It proved a
seminal paper in the study of Big Bang nucleosynthesis and,
although it was later shown to be correct only for the forma-
tion of hydrogen and helium (all the other elements are formed
inside stars), it is widely regarded enough to be known simply
as the alpha-beta-gamma ($\alpha\beta\gamma$) paper after the uncanny resemblance of the authors' names to the first three letters of the
Greek alphabet.

However, the coincidence is not quite what it seems. The
majority of the work for the paper was done by a young research
scientist, Ralph Alpher, who was supervised in his work by
George Gamow. When it came to publication Gamow looked
at the author list and, in his own words: 'It seemed unfair to
the Greek alphabet to have an article signed by Alpher and
Gamow only.' It suddenly occurred to Gamow that he could

(almost) insert the missing beta – the eminent physicist Dr Hans A. Bethe. And so the covering letter explaining the findings went in, signed by Alpher, Bethe (in absentia) and Gamow.

Initially at least, Ralph Alpher was dismayed to see that the name of another senior scientist, who had contributed absolutely nothing towards the work, had been added to the author list simply as a joke, while Gamow's first concern was what would happen when Bethe saw the paper. In this he was lucky. Unknown to him, Hans Bethe was a reviewer for *Physical Review* and, by chance, had received a copy of the letter with his name in the author line. He was an old friend of Gamow's and probably appreciated the joke but, more importantly, he liked the ideas in the paper – indeed, he would go on to do his own work on this subject. Noting later that 'I felt at the time it was a rather nice joke and that the paper had a chance of being correct,' he simply struck out the words 'in absentia' and sent the paper back for publication.

So the great Alpher, Bethe, Gamow paper, now known simply as the $\alpha\beta\gamma$, became legend, despite the fact that one of the authors was never involved in the work. Gamow would later joke that the paper became so famous, in part thanks to the joke, that when it received some severe criticism Bethe considered changing his name to Zacharias to try to get away from the association.

When R.C. Herman joined the project, Gamow tried to further confuse matters by asking him to change his name to Delter so that their next work could be signed Alpher, Bethe, Gamow, Delter, but Herman declined. This didn't stop Gamow from later referring in another paper to 'the neutron capture theory . . . developed by Alpher, Bethe, Gamow and Delter'. Thankfully, with twenty letters of the Greek alphabet still to go, Gamow stopped there.

3

Chemistry, Conkers and Calamity

(In which things that shouldn't explode
do so and those that should don't.)

Chemistry is fun!

Joel Henry Hildebrand, quoted in Joseph Hirschfelder,
Annual Review of Physical Chemistry (1983)

So we come on to chemistry, a subject that often seems to impinge more directly on us than the theories of physics. And when I say impinge . . .

The smell

It began in June 1909, in the city of Cambridge. The university was, at that time, celebrating the centenary of the birth of one its most famous sons – Charles Darwin. As well as lectures and events, many colleges were holding garden parties and afternoon teas in his honour. It was at one of these, in a garden bordering on the field known as Parker's Piece, that 'the smell' first wafted into the delicate noses of the learned men and women of the university.

To call 'the smell' merely a smell would be something of an understatement. The inhabitants of Cambridge were used to bad smells; it was for that very reason that they had just invested a great deal of money in updating the city's mediaeval sewage system. This, however, was noticeably different. It was far more pungent and, even in the open air, with a moderate breeze blowing, it seemed to get stronger and stronger. There was only one thing to do. The party guests were moved inside and the doors and windows tightly shut.

The following day Christ's College tried to hold its centenary garden party but the fellowship here proved no more resilient and were driven indoors by the rich aroma that once again hung over the city. Soon 'the Smell' was the talk of the town. It had forced shopkeepers to shut early, ended numerous parties and teas, and put a stop to punting on the Cam. Those who had invested so heavily in the new sewage system feared the worst and wrote letters of protest to the council, demanding to know what was going to be done. The council, on the other hand, had no idea what was causing 'the Smell'.

Eventually it was the dogged reporters of the *Cambridge Daily News* who managed to solve the riddle, splashing the results of their investigation across the front page under the headline: 'What Was it? Suspected Drains Exonerated. Science the Sinner.'

And so it proved to be. To be fair, Professor Sir William Jackson Pope and his assistant John Read were aware that their experiments dealt with a fairly smelly substance and had taken every precaution to contain its vapours. They had fitted their apparatus with chemical traps and, for good measure, assembled the equipment on the roof of the chemistry faculty in Cambridge to ensure plenty of air was circulating. All the same, these precautions had proved woefully inadequate.

What interested Pope and Read was the shape of molecules. Pope had been instrumental in the development of what is known as stereochemistry – the study of how the atoms within a molecule can be arranged in different ways. Having done his pioneering work on carbon, Pope had moved on to sulphur compounds and was keen to see the effects of knocking out the middle sulphur atom in hydrogen sulphide and replacing it with the similar element selenium. Hydrogen sulphide is famous for smelling of rotten eggs, so it won't come as a shock to learn that the similar hydrogen selenide is possessed of a comparable odour.

What is less well known is the fact that the smell of hydrogen selenide is many thousands times worse. It was whilst trying to turn this foul-smelling substance into the more innocuous but long-winded methylethylselenetine bromide that some of the gas escaped, releasing what the experimenters themselves referred to as 'a sensational odour'. This noxious cloud had then drifted downwind from the chemistry faculty and across the lawns of Cambridge where it had met with an understandably hostile reception.

Obviously the experiment couldn't continue with the whole city up in arms about 'the Smell', so the chemists removed their work to a field near Clayhithe in the middle of the sparsely populated Fens. Here they hoped to be able to work in peace, yet even on the open, windswept Fens, the 'thunderous smell', as Read put it, became too much for them. Not only were the barge- and boat-owners on the nearby river stunned by the terrible odour but it also began to have an unusual effect on the local fauna. A herd of cows began to show an enthusiastic interest in the origin of the smell. Read noted: 'creeping and flying insects of many kinds swarmed over the apparatus, some of them even making determined attempts to force a way past the stoppers into the flasks. Their whole behaviour indicated that they felt they were missing something really good.'

This was enough even for the experimenters who packed up their equipment and decided to move on to studying other, less odorous, molecules in sweeter-smelling pastures.

∽

On the subject of smells, not every
smell in chemistry is a bad thing. Or, rather,
even some bad smells can produce good results
as Robert Boyle found out when a German
smeared urine on his face.

∽

The icy nightlight

In September 1677, the alchemist Daniel Kraft arrived in London at the specific invitation of King Charles II, prompted by a rumour from the court of Duke Johann Frederick of Saxony. The word was that Kraft had perfected a technique for creating an astonishing new material that, when kept under water, glowed in the dark without ever dimming and which, on exposure to air, immediately burst into flames.

Whilst nobody knew how this might be useful, for anyone interested in alchemy it seemed like a promising line of enquiry and so the king directed Kraft to the garden laboratory of the greatest chemist he knew – Robert Boyle (see page 19). In his laboratory Boyle had gathered together other members of the Royal Society for a demonstration of this marvellous new material, and Kraft did not disappoint. In Boyle's own notebooks, he recorded how the material was mixed in a round flask of water, making the whole bowl glow eerily and flash with fire. Kraft, quite the showman, scattered particles of the material on the carpet, greatly troubling Boyle as it was a particularly fine Turkish specimen, and there it glowed like a thousand stars but, to his great relief, caused no damage.

Kraft then smeared the material on his finger and wrote the word 'Domini' in glowing letters on the wall before rubbing some more on to Boyle's face and hands, making the great man himself glow a deathly green. Boyle noted that the material shone with 'a mixture of strangeness, beauty and frightfulness'. Only one part of the demonstration miscarried. Kraft attempted to make one piece ignite spontaneously on contact with air and to get another to set light to a small pile of gunpowder, but these experiments failed. Never one to let his audience down, Kraft returned a few days later and successfully completed the demonstration.

For Kraft the wonder material was the meat and drink of a showman – a miracle to be displayed in the courts of Europe for the amazement of kings and councillors, as well as a nice little money-earner into the bargain. Boyle, however, was not an alchemist in Kraft's mould; he was of a new breed of gentleman scientist – a founder and council member of the Royal Society, as well as the discoverer of Boyle's Law (that the absolute pressure of a gas is inversely proportional to its volume at constant temperature in a closed system). He wanted to know what this substance actually was and how he could make it.

Naturally enough, he began by politely asking Kraft, but Kraft was no idiot, nor was he daft enough to leave a sample with Boyle. He had, after all, charged the substantial fee of 1,000 thalers for his demonstration so he was hardly likely to reveal the secret for free. All he would say was that it came from something 'that belonged to the body of a man'.

This actually proved a surprisingly useful hint and, combined with Boyle's observation that it smelt of sulphur and onions when it was smeared on his face, he reasoned that it might have been derived from human urine. It would take two years for him and his assistants to crack the secret.

Working for Boyle was not always easy. After several months of thought, his assistant Daniel Bilger was told to begin collecting and boiling down large quantities of human urine to make a paste. Having produced this rather unpleasant substance, Boyle wasn't sure what to do next with it, so he asked that the same procedure be done on human excrement. This produced a still more foul material but not the magical glowing 'icy noctiluca' or 'icy nightlight', as Boyle had christened the unknown chemical. It would be nice to say that the breakthrough came from a brilliant piece of analytical chemistry on Boyle's part, or even from a lucky accident that released Bilger from his excrement boiling duties, but instead it was brought about by good old-fashioned cheating.

Late in 1678, Boyle met and hired the German alchemists, Johann Becher and his assistant Ambrose Godfrey Hanckwitz. They couldn't make 'noctiluca' either but they knew someone who could. Hennig Brandt was known in Germany as the man who had sold Kraft his samples. It turned out that the two men had been in business together for some time before Brandt realised he was being cheated. Although Kraft had been only the showman and had not been told the secret, perhaps they could get it out of Brandt? Hanckwitz was packed off to Germany to meet him.

Brandt, not surprisingly, refused to simply hand over the formula. After his split with Kraft he'd gone into business with the German polymath Gottfried Wilhelm von Leibniz (see pages 78 and 197)and for a while it looked as if his fortune was made – until Leibniz's interest drifted elsewhere. Brandt had pressed on, certain that he was on to something of real value, something not merely to be given away. He did, however, give Hanckwitz another vital clue, saying that very high temperatures were needed. It was this that made all the pieces fall into place.

When Hanckwitz returned with the news, Boyle at last had all the necessary information. A hint from Kraft that the base substance was urine and the suggestion from Brandt that the residue needed to be heated provided him with enough to begin the experiments. The early results were mixed as the retort broke during the extreme heating but Boyle noticed in the wreckage a faint glow – the glow of the icy noctiluca, or, as we call it, phosphorus.

Applying the skills of a chemist, rather than the ritual of an alchemist, Boyle and Hanckwitz soon perfected a technique for producing phosphorus that was many times more efficient than Brandt's and thus required slightly less gargantuan quantities of urine.

Hanckwitz, who dropped his German surname to become Ambrose Godfrey, refined the process still further and later set up in business as London's only phosphorus producer (aided by his old boss Boyle). So in a way he became London's only really successful alchemist, making himself a substantial quantity of gold from turning the city's rivers of urine into highly saleable phosphorus. The business he founded survived until 1915.

୶

If physics is a mind game, chemistry is a performance art. The great thing about chemistry is that so much more of it can be seen in everyday life than, say, sub-atomic physics. Sometimes far too much.

୶

Rouelle's performance

Despite introducing the concept of a chemical 'base' as a substance that reacts with an acid to form a solid salt, Guillaume François Rouelle the Elder is almost unheard of today. Yet in his day he was the most popular chemistry demonstrator at the Jardin du Roi in Paris, his lectures, which started in 1738, regularly being attended by over 200 students, including such chemical luminaries as Antoine-Laurent de Lavoisier (see page 11).

However, what attracted so many to Rouelle's class was not quite what his bosses would have wished. Rouelle was an unlikely demonstrator. Tall and thin, he would arrive at his lectures in full morning dress, including a velvet jacket, a powdered wig and a hat. However, in the course of the lecture, his whole appearance and demeanour would change. As he became more and more animated, he would warm up and begin stripping off layers of clothing. The hat and wig would be discarded to reveal an untidy mass of red hair, the jacket would follow, along with the tie and waistcoat until, if he was sufficiently enthused with his subject, he finished the lecture completely dishevelled in little more than his shirt-tails.

If this wasn't enough, few who reached the end of one of his public demonstrations were quite sure what had actually happened during this chemical striptease. Although hugely enthusiastic, Rouelle was not especially clear in his explanations, other than when berating fellow chemists for their ignorance. Some complained that his language was coarse, to which he would retort: 'I'm sorry – Are we at the Academy of Beautiful Speech?' Others pointed out that he was vague and frequently wandered off topic. He also often simply wandered off.

Despite being a demonstrator, giving demonstrations was not his forte; indeed, he was rather clumsy and relied on his nephew and brother to actually do the experiments. When he wanted them to do their stuff, he would shout 'Nephew!' This was followed usually by a long silence, as neither nephew nor brother was wholly reliable and both might well fail to turn up. If this happened, Rouelle would be forced to go back to his laboratory himself and get the equipment he needed. Nonetheless, he did not feel the need to stop lecturing whilst he did this, so by the time he returned his audience had usually missed a large part of what he had to say.

When he did reappear his audience usually knew they were in for a lively time if the great man attempted an experiment himself. The French philosopher Denis Diderot attended his classes and described one such occasion: '"Messieurs," he addressed us, "one must proceed with the greatest of caution; one bit of charcoal too much would shatter the container and threaten to smother us."'

This certainly got the attention of the crowd, although it didn't appear to get the attention of Guillaume Rouelle. Just as he was making his dramatic announcement, he absent-mindedly overstoked the fire. Diderot described what happened next: 'the enormous glass container burst with a huge explosion; smoke filled the room and students soon found themselves outside in the garden, unable to return until their coughs and terror dissipated'. Fortunately for Rouelle, the chimney took most of the force of the blast, leaving him untouched save for his long-suffering wig, which was blown right across the room. With the smoke cleared and the wig firmly replaced, he imperturbably continued his demonstration.

∽

Whilst we're on the subject of
blowing things up . . .

∽

Bang goes that theory

In 1917 the Director of Propellant Supplies at the Ministry of Supply sent an unusual letter to British schools and children's clubs:

> Collecting groups are being organised in your district. Groups of scholars & boy scouts are being organised to collect conkers. Receiving depots are being opened in most districts. All schools, W.V.S. centres, W.I.s, are involved. Boy Scout leaders will advise you of the nearest depot where 7/6 per cwt is being paid for immediate delivery of the chestnuts (without the outer green husks). This collection is invaluable war work and is very urgent. Please encourage it.

The missive did not explain why the government had suddenly taken an interest in conkers, making the request seem all the more puzzling. Whilst horse chestnuts might have been the weapon of choice for the autumn playground, they seemed an unlikely ally on the Western Front. But thanks to one man that was exactly where they would end up.

Professor Chaim Weizmann (see page 38) of Manchester University was a chemist working in a highly novel field. Having trained in Germany and Switzerland before the war, he had had something of a revelation whilst visiting his future brother-in-law at the Pasteur Institute in Paris. Here he was shown an astonishing new way of making basic chemicals, not by reacting one with another, but by using bacterial fermentation to break down organic material into its constituent parts.

Weizmann initially wondered whether this process could be used to make butanol, which he required for his research into synthetic rubber, by fermenting potatoes in a bacterial broth to create acetone, butanol and ethanol (ABE). Whilst the project hadn't been a great success, largely due to disagreements with his colleagues, the idea itself was sound. An added bonus was that along the way he had discovered the bacterium *Bacillus granulobacter pectinivorum*, now known by the no more catchy name of *Clostridium acetobutyculum* – an organism that could turn cereals such as maize into acetone, butanol and ethanol. With the outbreak of hostilities in 1914 it would come into its own.

The one thing absolutely necessary for prosecuting the First World War was explosives, and in Britain the explosive of choice for shells was cordite. Cordite had a great advantage over the old gunpowder in that it was smokeless, so those using it could see where they were shooting without being seen (and thus shot) themselves. It was made by mixing guncotton (nitrocellulose) and nitroglycerine with the lubricant Vaseline and the volatile solvent acetone. The mixture was then extruded into 'strings' that could be bound together into cords – hence the name 'cordite'.

By 1917 the British government's supplies of acetone were running dangerously low. Acetone was itself derived from a complex chemical reaction involving large quantities of wood and had traditionally been imported from Europe. The war had put a stop to European supplies so Britain had to look to making its own. That was where Chaim Weizmann came in.

In 1915, C.P. Scott of the *Manchester Guardian* had introduced Weizmann to David Lloyd George, who was minister of munitions. Hearing of the need for raw materials, Weizmann had suggested that the ABE fermentation method might be of interest, as one of its byproducts was acetone. He was duly given some resources to develop the technique as well as the use of a gin distillery in Bow, London, where he managed to scale up the process successfully until he could produce 228 tons of acetone a month.

His success, however, led to its own difficulties. By 1917, foodstuffs were also in short supply and using cereals that could feed the population to feed bacteria instead became increasingly hard to justify. Weizmann was asked to find some other starch source for his bacteria to feast on. To the dismay of schoolchildren everywhere the solution he came up with was the humble conker. The country was full of horse-chestnut trees whose plentiful fruit was of no other use than as a children's game. Yet inside every shiny brown shell, conkers were packed with starch. Six huge silos were built to receive the bounty and the message went out to schools and scout groups everywhere. Even the smallest and humblest members of society could now do their bit for the war effort, putting their playground games aside and handing over their precious conkers to make explosives.

During 1917, 3,000 tons of conkers were collected but the children's sacrifice proved unnecessary. Horse chestnuts foamed terribly when fermented, making the process particularly difficult to control and, besides, the building of acetone plants in Canada and the USA, where cereals were plentiful, soon covered all Britain's needs. Weizmann, who had helped to keep the guns firing, would go on to become a leading Zionist and the first president of Israel, with the support of a grateful British government, whilst children everywhere could at last get back to their games of conkers.

❧

Whilst not all chemists love explosions,
they are all dreamers. Indeed, all scientists
are dreamers to some extent but chemistry
is peculiar in having so many who actually
attribute their greatest work to ideas that
come to them while they are taking a nap.

❧

Mendeleev's dream

It is still a matter of conjecture how Dmitri Mendeleev hit upon
the idea for ordering the elements into a periodic table. Most
scientists would probably be happy to claim that the breakthrough was the fruit of years of hard work, or emerged in a
moment of brilliant insight, but Mendeleev maintained it came
to him in a dream.

It is certainly true that Mendeleev was trying to find some
hidden order in the elements. In his 1870 book *Principles of
Chemistry* he had noted that there seemed to be patterns in the
properties of elements. This was not in itself a new idea. In
1865, John Newlands had published his 'law of Octaves', in
which he ordered elements by atomic weight and noted that each
element bore a similarity to the corresponding element eight
places away from it in his table. This in itself followed on from
an observation made by the German chemist, Johann Döbereiner
(see page 138), around 1817.

The drawback of all these previous tables was that none of
them really worked as none allowed spaces for elements that
were yet to be discovered (and new ones were being discovered
all the time). Mendeleev decided to attack the problem by playing
cards, a favourite game of his, but the cards he used were marked

with the elements, their atomic weight (then only crudely measured) and their valency. With these he would play his arcane game of patience, hoping that the hidden order of nature would reveal itself to him in one hand.

Patience is a restful game and, after reordering his cards obsessively for three days and three nights, he wrote that when he finally nodded off, 'I saw in a dream a table, where all the elements fell into place as required. Awakening I immediately wrote it down on a piece of paper.'

Judging from his notes, however, the arrangement of the Periodic Table, as it became known, formed in his mind more slowly although he had already worked it out fairly well by the time the dream supposedly happened. It is true that after a lunchtime nap he decided to arrange the table vertically (as it is now) rather than horizontally, so perhaps that prompted the notion of the dream. He was not, after all, the only scientist to prefer to credit all his greatest achievements to idle dreaming (see page 86).

What was revolutionary about Mendeleev's table was that it had gaps in it, allowing for him to hypothesise as yet unknown elements, predicting their atomic weight and properties. He was not putting the known elements into *a* table but fitting them into *the* Periodic Table. The spaces below boron, aluminium and silicon he attributed to unknowns that he called eke-boron, eke-aluminium and eke-silicon, predicting their properties. The first of these was discovered in 1875 when Paul-Émile Lecoq de Boisbaudran announced that he had found an element with the exact properties Mendeleev had predicted for eke-aluminium – an element he christened gallium. Eke-boron (scandium) followed in 1879 and eke-silicon (germanium) in 1886.

The discovery of the Periodic Table laid the foundations of modern chemistry and made Mendeleev an international celebrity, so much so that Tsar Alexander III even forgave him his bigamy, Mendeleev not being the only scientist to take the view that the more, the merrier (see page 277). Having fallen in love with his niece's best friend and threatened to commit suicide if she didn't marry him, he had married her a month before officially divorcing his first wife. Worse still, the Russian Orthodox Church required a full seven-year gap after a divorce before a new marriage could be entered into. This might have led the Russian Academy of Science to block his membership, but it didn't bother the Tsar. When asked why he tolerated this orthodox outrage he replied simply: 'Mendeleev has two wives, yes, but I have only one Mendeleev.'

✥

If Mendeleev's reasons for putting it
all down to a dream are hard to fathom,
the dreams of August Kekulé may have
had a more practical motive . . .

✥

The (other) dreaming chemist

Today, August Kekulé's name is not well known outside chemical circles but we have him to thank for unravelling the knotty issue of how molecules are constructed. And he did this, so he always claimed, thanks to two dreams.

In the mid-nineteenth century, the problem faced by Kekulé and all other chemists was, on the face of it, simple. They could analyse molecules to find out what elements they were made of, but they often found that apparently different molecules with different properties were made up of the same number and type of atoms. How was this possible? Surely if a molecule contained the same elements, it must make the same thing?

This thought was running through August Kekulé's mind as

he sat on the open top deck of a horse-drawn Clapham omnibus late in the summer of 1855, on his way back to his lodgings, which, handily enough, were in Clapham. He had spent the evening, as he so often did, with his friend and fellow chemist Hugo Mueller and they had been discussing exactly this riddle. Now, sitting in the warm evening air, Kekulé began to nod off and fell to dreaming. It was only the conductor's cry of 'Clapham Road' that woke him from his reverie with a start. He dashed off the bus and headed quickly for home to begin putting down his revelations on paper, for on that brief bus journey he had had the dream of a lifetime. He later wrote of it:

I fell into a reverie, and lo, the atoms were gambolling before my eyes. Whenever, hitherto, these diminutive beings had appeared to me, they had always been in motion. Now, however, I saw how, frequently, two smaller atoms united to form a pair: how a larger one embraced the two smaller ones; how still larger ones kept hold of three or even four of the smaller: whilst the whole kept whirling in a giddy dance. I saw how the larger ones formed a chain, dragging the smaller ones after them but only at the ends of the chain.

Lesser men might have had a stiff whisky and called it a day, but for Kekulé the dream opened the door on to his structural theory of chemistry. In this he deduced how molecules – carbon molecules in the case of his work – could be made up of chains of atoms that might be arranged in different ways to form different molecules with different properties. By assigning a position to each atom in the molecule, and by connecting each with what he called 'affinity units' (today known as 'bonds'), he provided the first clear way of visualising molecules, opening up the world of structural chemistry.

Kekulé was not yet done with dreaming, however. Several

years passed, in which he became a celebrated chemist, holding the chair in chemistry at the University of Ghent, before he had his next great dream. In his own words:

> During my stay in Ghent, I lived in elegant bachelor quarters in the main thoroughfare. My study, however, faced a narrow side-alley and no daylight penetrated it . . . I was sitting writing on my textbook, but the work did not progress; my thoughts were elsewhere. I turned my chair to the fire and dozed. Again the atoms were gambolling before my eyes. This time the smaller groups kept modestly in the background. My mental eye, rendered more acute by the repeated visions of the kind, could now distinguish larger structures of manifold conformation; long rows sometimes more closely fitted together all twining and twisting in snake-like motion. But look! What was that? One of the snakes had seized hold of its own tail, and the form whirled mockingly before my eyes. As if by a flash of lightning I awoke; and this time also I spent the rest of the night in working out the consequences of the hypothesis.

What had apparently prompted this dream was Kekulé's work on another carbon molecule: benzene. By 1865 everyone knew what was in benzene – namely six carbon atoms and six hydrogen atoms – but how they were arranged continued to puzzle. Thanks to Kekulé's second dream it now became clear: benzene was ring-shaped.

Understanding the structure of benzene might not seem all that impressive after having laid the foundations of structural chemistry, but this molecule lay at the heart of organic chemistry, making Kekulé the most celebrated chemist of his day. His reasons for choosing to attribute all his best ideas to dreams remained a mystery to everyone – except perhaps fellow chemist Archibald Scott Couper.

Couper had independently come up with the idea of self-linking carbon atoms but, due to a misunderstanding with his boss at the faculty of medicine in Paris, his paper had been delayed; as a result Kekulé published first and hence received priority. Couper never overcame the disappointment and suffered a nervous breakdown, whilst Kekulé could maintain that, whatever Couper had discovered, he had already dreamt it all long before.

✺

Perhaps some chemists are so keen
to gain priority through dreams because
chemistry can be a very profitable subject, being
the origin of so many industrial processes.
Hitting this jackpot requires not only dazzling
intelligence, but a little serendipity.

✺

Perkin's luck

The life of William Henry Perkin just goes to show just how far a lucky break can take you, although it must be said that a dash of brilliance also helps.

The son of a London carpenter, Perkin developed a precocious talent for science at school and in 1853, aged just fifteen, he was accepted into the Royal College of Chemistry, where he began to study under the guidance of August Wilhelm von Hofmann (see page 151).

At the time, Hofmann was working on a substitute for quinine. As the British empire spread around the globe, the British came more and more into contact with one apparently unvanquishable opponent – malaria. There were few weapons in the medical arsenal against this debilitating and often fatal disease, but the most useful was quinine. Quinine, however, was derived from the bark of the South American cinchona tree, making it a rare and expensive product. What the British empire needed was a synthetic quinine that was cheap and easily available.

The task proved difficult (in fact, a formal chemical synthesis of the drug wasn't achieved until 1944). Having failed to make progress, Hofmann decided to return to his native Germany for a break in the Easter of 1856. This was the ambitious Perkin's opportunity and, like the sorcerer's apprentice, he grabbed it. Still only eighteen, he decided that while his boss was away he would synthesise quinine himself and set to work in his own rather haphazard laboratory at his home in Cable Street.

His idea was to oxidise a salt of allytoluidine with potassium dichromate but the experiment was not a success. Undaunted, he tried again, this time substituting aliline, derived from coal tar, for the allytoluidine. As Hofmann had been working on petroleum derivatives, which he believed to have a similar structure to quinine, this seemed like a good bet. It wasn't and the experiment failed again.

All that Perkin was left with was a thick, dark sludge, which, according to his own reports, he was about to throw away when it occurred to him to try dissolving it in alcohol. The result was unexpected, as the solution proved to be a rich purple colour. Purple, it just so happened, was one of the hardest colours to source to dye cloth. The Romans had used the mucous secretions of a predatory sea snail, the spiny dye-murex, for the purpose of making what they called Tyrian purple, but it had to be collected by hand and could be afforded only by the very wealthy. The techniques for its extraction had since been lost, probably in the thirteenth century, after which purplish reds were derived from cochineal, a ground-up scale insect.

Perkin was intrigued with his colour and its potential uses. By now he had obviously deviated from the plan to synthesise quinine, so he continued his work in secret, aided by his friend Arthur Church. Having convinced themselves that they had created a potential commercial dye that was safe, light-fast and could be made on an industrial scale, they christened the substance 'aniline purple'. Samples were sent to the Pullars dye works in Perth, Scotland, and Robert Pullar wrote back enthusiastically, encouraging them to go into full-scale production. In August 1856, Perkin took out a patent (number 1984) on what was the first synthetic aniline dye and, with a fond wave to all those who had nurtured his chemical genius, promptly resigned from the Royal College of Chemisty to go into business.

With the help of his father's money and his brother Thomas's talents, he began manufacturing the dye commercially, some-times marketing it as 'Tyrian purple' in reference to the ancient dye used in Roman emperors' togas. Later the French would christen the colour mauve, from the French word for the mallow flower, and from this chemists would derive their own term – mauveine. But there was still much work to be done. If Perkin had had a lucky break he was not a man to rest on his laurels, Roman or otherwise. Whilst the dye set well on silk, to work on cotton (a far more popular and available material) he would need to develop a mordant (a chemical that helps the dye bind to the cloth), which without further ado he did.

For Perkin it was the start of a life in industrial chemistry, leading to a complete transformation of the world of dyeing and, hence, the world around us. The naturally derived and often rather soft colours used until then in clothing and upholstery were soon replaced with a battery of intense synthetic aniline dyes, resulting in an explosion of colour into the Victorian world. Perkin for his part would go on to become one of the most honoured chemists of his day, receiving a knighthood, a fellowship of the Royal Society and a host of honorary doctor-ates from universities around the world.

By 1906, the year before his death, the *New York Times* in an interview with the great man estimated that $100,000,000 was invested in Perkin's discoveries in the US alone. In grateful thanks, the American section of the Society of Chemical Industry instituted the Perkin Medal for 'innovation in applied chemistry resulting in outstanding commercial development'. The first award went to Perkin himself.

∽

Although Perkin's genius was to quickly realise the industrial application for his novel bit of chemistry, in the field this is not universally the case. Unlike in physics, a discovery in chemistry is not always the answer to the question but may be just the start of a much longer process: trying to work out what the hell this new discovery is good for.

∽

Sticky stuff

It was 1968 and Spencer Ferguson Silver was not having the best time of it as a chemist at the Minnesota Mining and Manufacturing Company (now known simply as 3M). He'd invented a glue that wasn't very sticky but which had some unusual properties. The question was: what application is there for a not-very-sticky glue?

His glue was actually rather clever (for a glue), being formed of tiny spheres of acrylic that would form a surface bond strong enough to hold, say, pieces of paper together, but which could be peeled off with ease and, most importantly, could then be repositioned without tearing and without leaving a sticky mess behind. To Silver, this was clearly a breakthrough but few of his colleagues agreed with him. After all, what is the use of a glue that doesn't stick permanently and sticks only paper? There were already plenty of paper glues available and they were not only cheap but had the advantage of providing a permanent bond.

There followed nearly six years of attempting to overcome this magnificent indifference, in which Silver suggested the glue might be used to surface billboards or made into a spray for mounting photographs, but with no joy. By now just about every researcher at 3M had heard Silver's seminar on his low-tack adhesive, including Arthur Fry. Initially the talk hadn't affected him more than any of the others but suddenly it came back to him as he sat in church on a Sunday in 1974, listening to a, frankly, less than thrilling sermon.

In truth, Art Fry wasn't listening to the sermon at all; he was thinking about the tribulations of singing in the church choir and, in particular, about the burning issue of bookmarks. Choir members obviously had to be able to turn quickly to the hymns for each service, as and when they were needed, and so placed paper bookmarks in the relevant pages. However, when the organ struck up, the choir would stand and open their books, at which point all the bookmarks for all the other hymns would flutter gracefully to the floor. What was needed, Fry thought, was a way of making a sticky bookmark that wouldn't ruin the page – which brought him back to Silver's seminar on his not-very-sticky-adhesive.

The following week Fry managed to get a sample of the glue from Silver and painted it on to one edge of small paper bookmarks. This seemed to work well but it was when he needed to leave a quick note for his boss that the value of the idea finally dawned on him. Sticky notes, with a pressure-sensitive adhesive that didn't leave a mess but could be posted anywhere, were invaluable and soon everyone in 3M wanted samples for their own use. It would take another six years to perfect the manufacture of the little yellow sticky notes but in 1980 the Post-it note was launched and took up residence on every desk.

◈

The Post-it note shows that chemistry can lead to unexpected places, but it can also lead unexpected people there too . . .

◈

Bulletproof

Stephanie Kwolek hadn't really wanted to be a chemist. That is not to say that she didn't have an interest in science; far from it. She remembered as a child walking through the woods with her father, looking for plants and animals to study, and this had inspired her to take a degree from Margaret Morrison Carnegie College (the women's college for Carnegie Mellon university) in general science.

However, what she really wanted to be was a doctor. In 1946, having graduated, she realised it wasn't going to happen, at least not yet. Studying medicine was expensive and her father had died when she was just ten years old, leaving her mother to raise her during the Great Depression. Being a doctor would cost money she didn't have.

What she did have was a good degree majoring in chemistry, which got her a job at the French-sounding but very much American chemical firm, E.I. du Pont de Nemours and Company (known more concisely as DuPont). DuPont was then at the forefront of research into synthetic fibres. Just eight years earlier it had brought the first of these, nylon, to market and its

'Pioneering Research Laboratory' was on the lookout for bright young scientists. Thanks to the war, these no longer had to be drawn just from the ranks of men, so Kwolek got the job. In some ways it was a dream come true, as Kwolek had inherited a love of fabrics and clothing from her mother as well as a love of science from her father. At DuPont she would be able to indulge both.

Science, of course, takes time. It was 1964 before she had her great breakthrough and it came from the most unlikely of starts. The brief from management was to find a lightweight, ultra-strong fibre to replace the steel in radial tyres. As there were rumours of an oil crisis, the concept was that lighter, stiffer car tyres would use less fuel, so it was considered a worthwhile area to explore if far less glamorous than, say, nylon. No one was keen to take it on. Whilst women were employed at DuPont, they weren't always treated equally with the men – it took fifteen years for Kwolek to even get a promotion – so, not surprisingly perhaps, she was given the task rather than one of her male colleagues.

Kwolek began working with a very unusual substance, the first synthetic polymer shown to form liquid crystals (a state of matter with properties somewhere between those of a conventional liquid and those of a solid crystal). Furthermore, the molecular chains that the polymer formed weren't flexible like most others, but stiff, like tiny sticks. At first, the solution she created looked decidedly unpromising. For one thing it was cloudy, suggesting that there were solid particles in it, and it was also runny where most polymers were viscous. Most chemists could have been forgiven for throwing it away and starting again, but instead Kwolek took a sample to be spun into thread in the company spinneret.

This appeared to be another mistake. The man in charge refused to spin the cloudy liquid as, he claimed, it clearly had solid particles in it that would clog up the 0.0001-inch holes in his machine. Kwolek filtered the solution but it remained resolutely cloudy. Undaunted, she asked again, and again. Eventually, as she put it: 'I think either I wore him down or else he felt sorry for me.'

As it turned out, the solution didn't clog the spinneret. On the contrary, it spun easily into an incredibly strong fibre. This was sent off to be tested in another lab, which reported back that the fibre was, astonishingly, five times stronger than steel and resistant to corrosion, wear and fire. Thinking the results to be a mistake, she sent another sample, but that came back with the same outcome. Once she had published the results internally, a group was set up to study this new group of polymers whose stiff molecules were shown to line up when spun to form remarkably strong fibres. The most promising of these was now developed for market and, in 1971, Kwolek's fibre, Kevlar, was finally launched.

Although the tyre industry did not take to the invention, as it would involve replacing large amounts of manufacturing equipment while steel (and oil) were still cheap, the material nevertheless found its way into many other industries. Extraordinarily tough and light, Kevlar was soon a component in everything from crash helmets to boat hulls, suspension bridge supports and sports equipment.

Most famously of all, Kevlar proved so strong that it could stop a bullet or deflect a knife blade, making it the main material in bulletproof and stab-proof jackets. To date, the Kevlar Survivors Club has over 2,700 members who owe their lives to Kwolek's unpromising fibre. In 1997, she was awarded the Perkin Medal (see page 92) for her work. Despite never becoming the doctor she had once wanted to be, she had saved more lives than many who had.

༄

Synthesising the unexpected is an occupational
hazard for chemists – not that the chemical
result is necessarily unexpected – but it is often
entirely unknown how a new substance will
behave. This can prove rather exciting . . .

༄

Hofmann's ride

There is a lot of confusion surrounding the discovery of LSD,
which is perhaps appropriate for a drug that had such a profound
effect, not least on its discoverer.

Contrary to popular legend, Swiss chemist Albert Hofmann
did not discover LSD by accident. In 1938, he was working for
Sandoz Laboratories, analysing the constituents of plants and
funguses to see whether any useful pharmaceutical drugs could
be derived from them. In particular he had been looking at the
fungus ergot, which grows on rye and other cereals. Ergot was
known to contain powerful chemicals, being the chief agent
responsible in the number of recorded cases of ergotism – or
poisoning from the fungus, which could lead to hallucinations,
mania, psychosis and the development of dry gangrene.

From working with ergot, Hofmann had derived the alkaloid
ergotamine and from this its precursor, lysergic acid. He then
set to work analysing the various derivatives of this, numbering
each 'Lysergic Acid Derivative' as he went. When he got to LSD-
25 (Lysergic Acid Diethylamide), he hoped to have found a
circulatory stimulant as it had a similar structure to another
known stimulant. When the drug was tested on animals, it was
noted that they became 'restless', but no useful effects were
recorded and the trials were stopped.

So LSD might have been synthesised, tested and put away for ever, were it not for what Hofmann later called a 'peculiar presentiment'. For some reason, five years later, Hofmann decided to return to his work on the very unpromising LSD-25. During his resynthesis of the molecule, he somehow accidentally came into contact with the drug, possibly absorbing a small amount through his skin, and was forced to stop work when he became dizzy. Aware that the drug, with its then unknown effects, might be the cause, he decided to go home and there, as he records in his diary:

> I lay down and sank into a not unpleasant intoxicated-like condition, characterized by an extremely stimulated imagination. In a dreamlike state, with eyes closed (I found the daylight to be unpleasantly glaring), I perceived an uninterrupted stream of fantastic pictures, extraordinary shapes with intense, kaleidoscopic play of colours. After some two hours this condition faded away.

Hofmann was fascinated by the experience, astonished that such a tiny quantity of such an apparently unpromising substance could cause such effects. Further testing on humans would of course be highly unethical, so Hofmann decided to try a larger dose of the drug on himself.

Three days later, on 19 April 1943, Hofmann swallowed a 250-microgram dose of LSD, having guessed that this was around the threshold (or safe) dose. In fact, the threshold dose for LSD is 20 micrograms. He recorded in his laboratory journal that he soon began to experience dizziness and feelings of anxiety combined with a desire to laugh. When he found he could no longer write, he asked an assistant to take him home. As it was wartime and there were no cars available, this had to be by bicycle – a journey commemorated in the popular name for the events of 19 April – Bicycle Day.

During the ride Hofmann's symptoms intensified. As he later wrote: 'On the way home, my condition began to assume threatening forms. Everything in my field of vision wavered and was distorted as if seen in a curved mirror. I also had the sensation of being unable to move from the spot. Nevertheless, my assistant later told me that we had travelled very rapidly.'

There can have been few more alarming bike rides in history, but this trip was nowhere near over. At home he remained lucid enough to ask for milk as a potential antidote but, when his neighbour brought it for him, he perceived her as 'a malevolent, insidious witch with a coloured mask', which was a little unfair. Panic set in as the thought came to him that he was possessed by a demon and he believed he might be dying. A doctor was called but could find nothing wrong physiologically with Hofmann, save for his extremely dilated pupils and agitated state of mind.

Eventually the intense symptoms passed: 'I could begin to enjoy the unprecedented colours and plays of shapes that persisted behind my closed eyes. Kaleidoscopic, fantastic images surged in on me, alternating, variegated, opening and then closing themselves in circles and spirals, exploding in colored fountains, rearranging and hybridizing themselves in constant flux.'

Having finally slept, Hofmann awoke feeling unusually refreshed as though 'renewed life flowed through me', and with the realisation that he had come across a remarkably powerful new drug. What had not occurred to him was the notion that this extraordinary substance, with its beautiful hallucinations but also what he called its 'demonic aspect', would one day come to be taken for fun.

4

Biology, Booze
and Brown Dogs

(In which we grow mould, break statues, drink
beer and take too many drugs.)

*[The science of life] is a superb and dazzlingly lighted hall
which may be reached only by passing through a long and
ghastly kitchen.*

Claude Bernard, *An Introduction to the Study
of Experimental Medicine* (1865)

Biology and, in particular, its relevance
to human health have, not surprisingly,
been of overwhelming concern to scientists for
generations. As our desire to stay alive is likely
to encourage us to part with our money to those
who promise it, so biology has also become
the concern of every quack, huckster and
purveyor of spring-loaded furniture.

The artificial horse

The English Malady was, according to George Cheyne, no more than an unfortunate side-effect of the wealth and ease to which so many in the mid-eighteenth century now found themselves accustomed. It was a disease unknown in harsher times, he assured his patients, and one for which they had only themselves to blame, for the English Malady was to fall prey to luxury and indolence or, as we would call it, obesity.

Cheyne was one of the most celebrated physicians of his day, not least because he chose to promote preventative medicine rather than simply deal with symptoms. His books exhorted the public to stay healthy, get plenty of exercise and eat sensibly. He himself knew only too well what happened if such advice was not followed for, as he told his readers, he once weighed 32 stone, was short of breath, ulcerous of leg and thoroughly depressed.

Obesity was not an uncommon condition in the period. International trade was making Britain rich, and people with money were indulging in more luxury and less exercise than ever before. To give an idea of just how much luxury, when Cheyne turned his own life around he records how, in place of the old excesses, he now rarely drank more than 'a quart or three pints of wine' a day. This was clearly meant to impress his audience as a sign of steely moderation. Sadly, he nowhere tells us how much wine he drank daily *before* he became so abstemious.

Cheyne's no-nonsense, practical approach won him many admirers, including writers, politicians and earls, who seemed to revel in his blunt advice to eat less and cheer up. As he told his wealthy readership: 'There is nothing more ridiculous than to see tender, hysterical and vapourish People, perpetually complaining, and yet perpetually cramming.'

Beyond simply promoting willpower, Cheyne was also the first to sponsor what is probably the earliest exercise machine in history. The British merchant and upper classes got their exercise from riding, but as a pleasure rather than a necessity, which meant only in good weather in the summer. At all other times potential riders would loll about in their houses, no doubt gorging themselves, or venture out solely in their carriages. This, in Cheyne's mind, was the cause of much of the problem – no one went riding in winter.

Nowhere does Cheyne imply that he invented the solution, but he certainly made it popular, and that solution was the chamber horse. It is unclear who should actually take the credit for thinking up the chamber horse, although the first recorded claim to have done so comes from Henry Marsh of Clare Market in 1739, the year before Cheyne first mentions it. The device consisted of a wooden chair frame with a deep, leather-uphol-stered seat inside which were a series of stacked springs sepa-rated by planks. The exerciser would sit in the chair, grasp the two posts attached to the front of the armrests and vigorously bounce up and down on the springs. This, it was said, simu-lated riding a horse.

It is perhaps debatable the degree to which bouncing on a chair and riding a horse are analogous but it certainly helped to shed the pounds. Cheyne also enthusiastically notes that, while getting exercise on the chamber horse, the bouncer can still read, direct servants or dictate letters – always assuming your staff could keep a straight face. He also recommends that two people might just as effectively bounce on the chair at the same time.

The craze for the chamber horse, like so many subsequent exercise crazes, didn't last, although John Wesley swore by it, or would have done if he had sworn at all. The contraption makes its last main appearance in literature in Jane Austen's unfinished novel *Sanditon*. After this, chamber horses seem to have been relegated to the attic, like so many exercise bikes and rowing machines of later generations.

Biology can be one of the riskiest sciences as, in the case of medical advances, the experimental test-bed is, ultimately, a living human being. For the scientists whose gamble pays off, the rewards can be academic immortality. We don't like to talk about the others, but it can be a damned close-run thing.

Mad dogs and Frenchmen

In the late nineteenth century, many common diseases were rightly feared and none more so than rabies, even though it was not, frankly, all that common. It owed its terrifying reputation to what it did to its victims.

Following infection, two to twelve weeks – sometimes much longer – might pass while the virus travelled to the central nervous system, before the first flu-like symptoms arose. These would be rapidly followed by any of a number of more frightening symptoms, including the hallucinations, mania and confusion that gave the disease its name, from the Latin *rabies* – madness. An inability to swallow liquids would follow, due to a creeping paralysis of the jaw and throat, succeeded by lethargy and coma. By the time most victims were worried enough to see a doctor, it was too late. Death was all but inevitable.

That was unless the doctor was Louis Pasteur (see page 109). The story of how this great man came to defeat rabies is as bold as it is alarming. By the mid-1880s, Pasteur was already a celebrated microbiologist, having discovered how to immunise cattle against anthrax by weakening (or attenuating) the bacillus before injecting it into animals. It was a technique that he knew could be expanded into 'vaccinating' other animals against other diseases (a term coined by Edward Jenner from his work on cowpox, the Latin for cow being *vacca*). However, trying on humans vaccines against deadly diseases would require a great deal of experimentation on animals first.

Or it would have done, had not an anxious mother brought a nine-year-old boy from Alsace to see Pasteur on 6 July 1885. Pasteur examined the little boy, Joseph Meister, and wrote in his notebook: 'Severely bitten on the middle finger of the right hand, on the thighs, and on the leg by the same rabid dog that tore his trousers, threw him down and would have devoured him had it not been for the arrival of a mason armed with two iron bars who beat the dog down.'

In total the boy had fourteen wounds. It seemed to those gathered in Pasteur's room that the child's terrible ordeal with the mad dog would now inexorably be followed by all the horrors of rabies itself. That, however, was not Pasteur's opinion.

Pasteur consulted with the neurologist Alfred Vulpian and the physician Jacques-Joseph Grancher about taking a radical step with his young patient. For some time he had been working on a rabies vaccine, made by slowly drying the spinal cords of rabid rabbits to weaken or kill the virus, before powdering it and injecting it into animals to provide them with immunity. He claimed to have had success with this method in vaccinating dogs, but was this terrible case enough of a justification to apply this relatively untried technique, with a deadly agent, on a small child? Vulpian and Grancher agreed with Pasteur – it was.

Pasteur began preparing a series of thirteen vaccinations to be administered over the next ten days, each with a progressively less dried, and hence more virulent, strain of rabies, taken from his rabid rabbits. In theory the increasing, but weakened, dose of rabies would give the boy's immune system a chance to recognise and destroy the virus before it took hold. At 11 a.m. on 16 July, Joseph Meister received the last vaccination, from a rabbit that had died only the previous day and whose spinal cord was still full of deadly rabies. The evening before, Pasteur's wife Marie wrote to their offspring: 'My dear children, this will be another bad night for your father. He cannot come to terms with the idea of applying a measure of last resort to this child, and yet now he has to go through with it. The little fellow continues to feel very well.'

And Pasteur did go through with it, inoculating the apparently healthy boy with the fatal virus. Two days later he retired to a safe distance, leaving his associates in Paris with instructions that the boy's progress should be reported to him. He believed that if the disease were to rear its ugly head, it would be some time in the next seven days, as was the case in rabbits. Seven days later, Joseph Meister was still healthy and was sent home to Alsace. He later became the gatekeeper at the Pasteur Institute.

The response to Pasteur's triumph was, perhaps surprisingly, mixed. The boy was well despite the ordeal and would never develop rabies, yet many questioned the apparently reckless injection of the child with a lethal disease when he was displaying no symptoms of having been infected in the first place. One of Pasteur's colleagues, Émile Roux, who actually created the vaccine, even temporarily left the Institute in protest at the experiment. Nevertheless, the inoculation of Joseph Meister was a landmark, demonstrating to many a whole new way of combating mortal diseases and marking a sea change in our understanding of the immune system.

So it is perhaps fortunate for Pasteur and science that the truth behind the Meister inoculations were not fully known at the time. Pasteur was always cagey about his work and insistent that his notebooks should always remain secret, which they did from his death in 1895 until 1971. Only then was the truth behind the Meister experiment revealed.

Pasteur had not been entirely honest with his results on rabies inoculation in animals. For one thing, the technique he used on Meister was untested and not the same one that he had previously employed on dogs. Nor had he been completely open about the outcome of his animal experiments. In those, the same number of untreated dogs had survived as that of treated dogs, making the results ambiguous at best. His notes also show that he had recommended vaccination for two rabies patients at a local hospital before Meister had come to him and one of them had died.

In truth, Joseph Meister may not have ever been infected with rabies, at least not before Pasteur knowingly injected him with the virus – many who are bitten by rabid animals are not. Even if he had been, the seven-day incubation typical of rabbits was nowhere near long enough for Pasteur to be sure that Meister was safe. Incubation in humans can be as long as two years. All the same, Pasteur was right about his theory of isolating and weakening or killing the infective agent in a disease before injecting it into a patient to 'prime' the immune system. It was a brilliant idea and Pasteur's fame quickly spread. It had been an audacious gamble, but it had worked and that, sometimes, can be the difference between fame and infamy.

༄

If Pasteur's experiments with inoculation might
seem reckless today, he might be forgiven,
bearing in mind what he did for beer. And the
ideas he got from sour beer would, incidentally,
change the face of medicine.

༄

Pasteur's little helpers

The predicament that would lead to one of the greatest ever
advances in medicine began not in a hospital but in a brewery.
In 1854 an enthusiastic but chronically underfunded Louis
Pasteur had just taken up the position of dean of the new science
department at the University of Lille. At only thirty-two, he was
the youngest dean in France and his chemistry classes attracted
a wide range of students from both academic and industrial
backgrounds.

One of the latter was Daniel Bigo, who introduced Pasteur to
the study of fermentation, thanks to his father's pressing problem.
Monsieur Bigo ran an industrial brewing facility at Esquermes
where he turned sugar beet into alcohol. It was a profitable business but still rather akin to alchemy, as it remained a mystery
exactly what it was that turned the mashed beets and yeast into
alcohol in the fermentation vats. Generally it was thought to be
some type of chemical reaction but, in Monsieur Bigo's case, it
was a reaction that was somehow going badly wrong.

Whilst some of his fermentation vats were producing alcohol
as usual, others seemed to be malfunctioning, producing a
stinking soup laced with lactic acid. In 1856, Monsieur Bigo
begged Pasteur to help discover the cause and Pasteur, in
desperate need of funding, was only too happy to oblige.

Pasteur took samples from both types of vat and examined them under the microscope, discovering that both were alive with microscopic, but different, particles (see page 269). The strange, rod-like organisms that appeared only in the tainted vats, he surmised, must be responsible for the taint. We now know that these were the lactic acid bacillus, which kills the yeast that is normally produced in the fermentation of alcohol, terminating the process and producing the stinking lactic acid soup instead.

To the modern mind this might seem obvious but at the time the idea that fermentation of any sort required a living organism, rather than just a chemical reaction was revolutionary. In his two works on the subject, 'Mémoire sur la fermentation appelée lactique' and 'Mémoire sur la fermentation alcoholique', he proved for the first time that fermentation was a biological process, something that came as a bit of a surprise to brewers everywhere.

But the brewing problem was only the start of Pasteur's work. Monsieur Bigo didn't just want an explanation, he wanted a cure, and Pasteur, realising that fermentation was produced by organisms, had an answer. If the beet mash was heated to a high enough temperature, any tainting bacteria that might have floated in it could be killed. The mash could then be cooled and sown with yeast as before. This process would, of course, go down in history as 'pasteurisation'.

Pasteur never lost his interest in fermentation, going on to address similar problems in the French wine industry in the mid-1860s, but it also planted a far more important seed in his mind. If a bacterium was responsible for lactic acid fermentation, perhaps specific micro-organisms were responsible for specific biological processes and, similarly, perhaps specific germs caused specific diseases. This 'germ theory' of disease, identifying microbes as the cause of infection rather than 'infected airs', 'miasmas' and 'bad water', would revolutionise medicine and surgery, ushering in the modern medical age. All thanks to a French brewer's problem and a scientist who, in his opening lecture at Lille, presciently told his audience: 'chance only favours the mind which is prepared.'

❧

The abiding image of biology is
not that of a Frenchman staring into a
beer barrel, which is perhaps a shame, but
the strange goings-on in Petri dishes. And
nothing in the history of science has become
more famous than what happened, by accident,
on Alexander Fleming's dish, thanks to
his dislike of washing up.

❧

Penicillin

The tale of the discovery of penicillin is one of the more argued over scientific stories of the twentieth century, filled as it is with contradictory characters, brilliant research and pure chance. What every schoolchild is told is that penicillin was discovered by Alexander Fleming, a research scientist working at St Mary's hospital in London. And that is probably the best place to begin.

Fleming was a dedicated but somewhat eccentric researcher. As his student V.D. Allison later recorded, whilst the students would faithfully clear up their work each evening, scrub down their bench, and wash and dry their used equipment, Fleming preferred a more serendipitous approach to research. He did not clean his bench, sometimes for months, nor did he wash up the Petri dishes on which he grew bacteria (and whatever else blew into the room), preferring instead to give them time to 'mature' so that he could study their varied flora and fauna later. This was not how science was meant to be done but, to Fleming's credit, it did sometimes work.

Fleming's first breakthrough came whilst studying the contents of his own nose. Suffering from a cold, he had decided to take some of his nasal mucus and culture it on a Petri dish. After two weeks of sitting on his bench, this dish had grown a splendid colony of golden bacteria – a contaminant that had probably floated in from the street outside. But right around the blob of nasal mucus the bacteria had refused to grow. What Fleming had discovered was the enzyme lysozyme, present in many bodily fluids, which dissolves cell walls. Unfortunately this proved to be of little clinical use and, after two years, the research moved on. Still, it was a start.

Fleming's next stroke of luck occurred in 1928. By now he was studying the colours of different strains of staphylococcus bacteria, by culturing all manner of infected fluids, from the contents of boils and skin abscesses to his old favourite, nasal mucus. Some of these he would even make into colourful 'pictures', composed entirely of bacteria, which he later delighted in showing to visiting dignitaries.

After several weeks' work preparing these samples, he went on holiday, leaving the now familiar pile of Petri dishes in the corner of the lab. When he returned in early September, one of his former students came by and asked how things were going with the experiment. By now even Fleming had decided to clean up a bit and most of the cultures were soaking in an anti-bacterial bath. Some of the pile had not made it past the water-line yet and were still 'live'. When he randomly picked up one of the plates, he suddenly noticed something he hadn't seen before: a small mound of mould had grown and around it all the staphylococcus bacteria had died.

The result intrigued Fleming, who showed the dish to a number of colleagues but, disappointingly, received little encouragement. Perhaps the fungus was a source of lysozyme? The mould was sent downstairs to the mycology department where it was identified as *Penicillium rubrum* – a non-toxic mould. Other moulds were now tested but *Penicillium*, later known as just penicillin, seemed the most interesting as it wasn't poisonous – indeed, Fleming even persuaded one of his students to eat some (see page 142). He reported that it tasted a bit like Stilton. More importantly, he didn't die.

There Fleming's simple story ends and the wrangling begins. Nine years passed in which Fleming had put the work on penicillin to one side, having had only inconclusive results. It was at Oxford that Howard Florey and Ernst Chain now picked up the trail, reading Fleming's original paper as part of their own investigations into lysozyme. It was no more than a piece of research, as the two later commented, and neither had any idea where it might lead, but after they were joined by Norman Heatley they quickly isolated penicillin and began testing it on bacterial infections in mice. Almost miraculously, mice given penicillin and then a 'fatal' dose of streptococcus bacteria survived, whilst those without the penicillin died. An Oxford policeman dying of sepsis volunteered to be a human guinea pig and began making an astonishing recovery before the supply of the mould ran out. He relapsed and, tragically, died.

It was now 1940 and the Second World War was hotting up, adding a dramatic impetus to their research. Many people even lightly injured, whether on the home front or fighting abroad, developed bacterial infections that often proved fatal, coming close to overwhelming the health service. But what if penicillin could save them? As things stood, only a tiny quantity of the mould had been produced. Realising that Britain could be invaded at any moment, the researchers swore to protect their 'miracle cure', smearing the mould on the inside of their coats to protect it from discovery by the Germans.

What was needed now was a way to make huge quantities of penicillin. Florey and Heatley headed for the USA with their precious mould, where facilities and finance existed to start mass production. So the antibiotic age began, although the arguments were far from over.

Fleming was now fêted worldwide, receiving hundreds of honorary degrees, fellowships at the world's most prestigious scientific institutions, a knighthood and a Nobel prize to boot, yet even he admitted that he was not sure he deserved it all. In truth, the discovery of the effects of penicillin on a discarded, dirty plate had been an absolute fluke, but it had required Fleming's eyes to see it. In turn it would be Florey and the Oxford group who had the vision to turn Fleming's chance discovery into the greatest breakthrough in medicine for centuries. However, the newspapers liked a hero, and preferably just one per discovery, and so the laurels for penicillin, at least in the popular imagination, remain Fleming's alone.

∽

Not all biology happens in a Petri dish or
even in a beer keg. Nor do the results of the
most diligent and useful work necessarily make
the scientist even a tiny bit famous. But fame
doesn't matter to a real scientist. Does it?

∽

Growing up

One of the surest signs that a house has once been a home to children must be the marks on doorframes, indicating the various heights they have achieved at various ages. Growing taller is a source of both pride and embarrassment to all youngsters, who simultaneously like to tower over their younger brethren whilst hating the 'Oh how you've grown' comments from doting relations.

However, measuring our children is more than just a habit; it can be a vital tool in checking that they are growing up healthy, as well as an early indicator when something might be going developmentally wrong. Yet this is not an ancient practice; indeed, it began only on the birth of a son to a eighteenth-century French naturalist.

That boy was born in 1759 to Philibert Guéneau de Montbeillard, friend and associate of the great French polymath Georges-Louis Leclerc, Comte de Buffon. De Montbeillard had been working with the comte on his gargantuan *Histoire naturelle, générale et particulière*, published between 1749 and 1788 in thirty-six shelf-buckling volumes: an attempt to produce a natural history of everything, although in the end limited to animals and minerals.

It was probably from the great natural historian that de Montbeillard got the idea for using his own child in an experiment. It was a simple but time-consuming task. Every six months of his son's childhood, he would carefully measure the boy's height, initially with the lad lying on a table, and then, when older, standing against a wall, just as a million parents have done since. Each of these figures he dutifully recorded and published in a table, covering his son's growth from birth to his eighteenth birthday in 1777.

As any parent can tell you, whilst the height of your own children is absolutely fascinating, the height of other people's is not. The results lay largely unread for 140 years until 1927, when Richard Scammon, a professor of foetal anatomy at the University of Minnesota, was looking for reliable data on the growth of children. He came across de Montbeillard's data set, converted it into metric measurements and, for the first time, plotted it on a chart of height against age. The result was the world's first childhood growth graph.

In 1942 this data set was again reinterpreted by Scottish biologist D'Arcy Thompson for his revised edition of *On Growth and Form*. He plotted it on a growth velocity chart, demonstrating that childhood growth is not constant but occurs at widely varying rates with age, including a huge growth spurt in the first two years and again at puberty, finally coming to a complete stop around the age of eighteen to twenty. This might seem obvious to us all today but, even in D'Arcy Thompson's time, de Montbeillard's measurements were one of the few reliable and complete sets readily available. Today they form the foundation of every growth chart in every childhood record, one of the fundamental benchmarks by which we monitor the healthy growth of our children.

And what of de Montbeillard's son? We know that he was an exceptionally strong boy for his time and even today would be on the 97th percentile for height, that he grew very normally, with a growth spurt in infancy and another aged fourteen, and that he stopped growing at eighteen, having reached a height of 180 centimetres. During that time his father monitored his growth, kept him safe from disease, even using the risky procedure of inoculating him with a small quantity of infected smallpox matter to provide him with resistance to the fatal scourge.

It was when he became an adult outside his father's control that his life took a tragic course. During the French Revolution he went to the guillotine on the orders of Robespierre, drastically altering his adult height but leaving behind the chart that would ensure the health of generations of children to come.

❧

As we saw earlier, experiments in biology
are so often performed on the living and as a
result it garners more protests than just about
any other scientific field. Few people have been
driven to violence by litmus paper, few have
railed against the injustice of gravity –
not when sober, anyway – but one small
brown dog can cause a riot.

❧

The Brown Dog Riots

The use of animals in medical experiments has long been a source of contention. The first legislation in Britain to control vivisection was enacted in 1876, but it has rarely reached such a fever pitch as it did in 1907.

The Brown Dog Affair, as it became known, started in the lecture halls of University College, London, in 1893. In that year, two Swedish anti-vivisection campaigners, Louise Lind-af-Hageby and Leisa K. Schartau, enrolled as medical students at the London School of Medicine for Women and began recording what they saw in the demonstration rooms of the university.

One event in particular stood out. They claimed that on one occasion they had arrived early for a dissection class being given by Dr William Bayliss (one of the discoverers of hormones) in which he intended to prove that salivary pressure was independent of blood pressure. He would do this by electrically stimulating the exposed nerve of a live dog's salivary gland. This was in no way an illegal procedure, as vivisection demonstrations on dogs were common and often considered a vital part of the education of medical students. But this time

Lind-af-Hageby and Schartau claimed there was something wrong.

In their diary they recorded that the brown dog brought into the theatre was not anaesthetised, as was required, and that it bore the unhealed scar from a previous experiment – when the law allowed only one experiment to be performed on each animal. They also claimed that the dog struggled violently to free itself during the demonstration whilst the gathered medical students laughed and joked. All this they reported to Stephen Coleridge, a barrister and famous anti-vivisectionist, who in turn gave a speech about the event that was duly reported in the newspapers. Bayliss, who denied any wrongdoing, was furious and demanded a full retraction. Coleridge, keen to test the case in court, refused and so Bayliss sued.

The trial, which began on 11 November 1903, garnered more publicity than perhaps any animal cruelty case before or since. University College's Professor of Physiology, Ernest Starling, was called and admitted that the first operation on the dog had been performed by him but that he had allowed a second (illegal) procedure only to prevent the death of a second dog. He also angrily denied the allegation that the animal was not anaes-thetised, pointing out that the anaesthetic was delivered by a pipe under the dissection table, which the women could not have seen. He also stated that such a delicate experiment would have been impossible on a conscious dog. Finally the university admitted that the dog had been killed afterwards by Henry Dale, later himself a Nobel prize winner, who, as he was still a student, was not technically licensed to put down the animal.

Bayliss's own defence was led by Rufus Isaac, later Viceroy of India, and proved that Bayliss himself had done nothing illegal – indeed, the 1876 Act specifically exempted such demonstra-tions and demonstrators from prosecution. To a packed gallery, the jury announced Coleridge guilty of libel and the judge ordered him to pay the modern equivalent of around £400,000 in damages and costs.

This was only the beginning of the affair. Coleridge soon raised this huge sum through donations and on its receipt Bayliss passed it all to the university for medical research. Yet the case would not rest there. Anti-vivisectionists demanded a memorial to the animal, so a water fountain was designed, carrying a bronze of the brown dog and the following inscription:

In Memory of the Brown Terrier Dog done to Death in the Laboratories of University College in February 1903, after having endured Vivisection extending over more than two months and having been handed from one Vivisector to another till Death came to his Release. Also in Memory of the 232 dogs vivisected at the same place during the year 1902. Men and Women of England, how long shall these things be?

Of course, finding a council that would take this somewhat inflammatory monument was not easy, but eventually Battersea, famed for its dogs' home and a local hospital that already banned vivisection, agreed. The statue was unveiled on 15 September 1906 in the presence of George Bernard Shaw.

Rarely has an inanimate lump of bronze caused more trouble. At night, groups of indignant medical students from the university would set out to demolish the statue, which they considered a dangerous affront to vital medical research. These 'anti-doggers' were met by a permanent police guard, as well as by an alliance of suffragettes and trade unionists, who identified the students with the establishment and themselves with the vivisected dog. These confrontations soon spread, with pro and anti marches through town, culminating in a 1,000-strong, anti-dogger march on 10 December 1907, which violently clashed with anti-vivisectionists and police in a series of running battles around Trafalgar Square. They later became known as the 'Brown Dog Riots'.

Eventually, Battersea Council – tired of the fighting, unwilling to pay for twenty-four-hour policing of a statue and in spite of a 20,000-signatory petition – quietly had the fountain removed and broken up in 1910. A new memorial to the brown dog was eventually set up in Battersea in 1985.

∾

Physics, you will remember, has sometimes been undertaken by people from unexpected backgrounds. Biological sciences might seem a less fertile ground for the keen amateur, requiring exotic equipment and materials, but in fact this couldn't be further from the truth. Whilst few individuals will pay for a proof of the laws of angular momentum, who could resist an elixir of life?

∾

Lily the Pink

Lydia Estes Pinkham was not a fraud, although the lavish claims made for her 'Vegetable Compound', both in real life and in song, might give that impression.

Lydia Pinkham was the tenth of twelve children born to an old Quaker family in Lynn, Massachusetts, in February 1819. In 1843 she married a local shoemaker and went on to have five children with him, the second of whom died in childhood. In terms of the time, she seemed headed for an uneventful life.

However, Lydia had been well educated and was active in her local community, both as a fervent abolitionist of slavery and as a supporter of women's rights. She became known for offering remedies for what were euphemistically known as 'female complaints', especially those associated with the menopause. In an era when doctors and medicines were far beyond the financial reach of many families, such herbal cures were common, as well as being more trustworthy than the potions peddled by itinerant 'quacks'. Lydia developed a reputation, only enhanced by the fact that she provided her services and her medicines entirely free.

What would change Lydia's life for ever was the financial crash known as the 'Panic of 1873', which ended the great American railroad boom. In it, Lydia's husband Isaac, who had never been very successful in business, was ruined and the stress of this destroyed his health. With Isaac unable to work, it fell to Lydia to bring some money into the family, so she began selling her remedies rather than giving them away. They proved so popular that, in 1875, the family went into business properly.

Three principal reasons account for the subsequent astonishing success of Lydia Pinkham's Vegetable Compound. First, there was Lydia's genuine belief in the efficacy of the remedy and the unusual level of care she gave her customers. In an age when 'female complaints' certainly weren't talked about in public, Lydia exhorted women to write to her in confidence about them. In return she would unfailingly reply, proffering sensible advice and often enclosing one of the pamphlets she had prepared on the subject. Needless to say, she would always also recommend a hefty dose of her Vegetable Compound.

Second, there was the Pinkhams' extraordinary advertising campaign. From 1876, Lydia put her own portrait on the bottle, showing her as a sensible and mature woman, and underneath she placed testimonials from satisfied customers. Adverts for her product sympathised with women's silent pain, claiming 'The Health of Women is the Hope of the Race', but also warned that any woman who would not take the time to write to Lydia for her free advice was 'responsible for her own suffering'. By 1878 these appeared in more newspapers and magazines than any other advertisement. The lack of advertising regulation meant that the remedy could be claimed as a cure for just about anything, from kidney disease to cancer. As the early bottles of the Compound modestly put it, Lydia's mixture was 'The Greatest Remedy in the World'.

Finally, there was the contents of the bottles. Lydia Pinkham's Vegetable Compound was probably based on recipes available in self-help medical books such as John King's *American Dispensary*, and contained a number of vegetable extracts such as unicorn root, black cohosh, pleurisy root and fenugreek, many of which are still used in complementary medicine. Perhaps a more important factor in providing the often sudden improvements in health and disposition claimed for the product was the 20 per cent alcohol content, making the preparation 40 per cent proof. As Lydia Pinkham's Vegetable Compound was marketed as a medicine, it could be reasonably taken by anyone, including the respectable and sober ladies of the Women's Christian Temperance Union, but, whether they knew it or not, it was a medicine that could get you splendidly drunk.

With many of the women (and men) of America knocking back a preparation stronger than most sherries, it is perhaps not surprising that Lydia Pinkham was making $300,000 a year by 1883, making hers the US's most popular patent medicine (although she never actually patented the product). That same year the company received a minor reverse with the death of Lydia herself, but that didn't stop the Compound from flying off the shelves.

More disturbingly, it didn't stop Lydia writing to her many correspondents, offering practical advice and recommending her cure. In 1905 the scam was finally exposed by *The Ladies Home Journal*, which published a picture of Lydia's grave and revealed that for twenty-two years correspondents had not been receiving letters from Lydia herself but from one of a pool of typists sending pro-forma responses. The Lydia E. Pinkham Company responded that they had never claimed Lydia was still alive but that in fact her daughter-in-law, Jennie Pinkham, was now in charge of replying to customers' letters.

A further blow to the company came with the passing of the Food and Drug Act of 1906, which rather unsportingly required all such preparations to declare their alcoholic content. Just before the law came in, Pinkhams reduced the dose in the Compound to around 13.5 per cent but this revelation still came as something of a shock to many fervent Temperance supporters who learnt, on reading the label, that they had largely been drunk for the past thirty years.

Despite the loss of support from the Temperance movement, it would be alcohol that would again save the day for the Pinkhams. The introduction of Prohibition in the US in January 1920 banned alcoholic beverages outright, but Lydia Pinkham's Vegetable Compound was a medicine and hence exempt. Suddenly everyone seemed a lot more interested in preserving their health and by 1935 the company was turning over $3.5 million a year.

It was also the Roaring Twenties that immortalised Lydia and her medicine for ever with the introduction of a drinking song to accompany the imbibing of cratefuls of the 'medicine'. Originally this was a rather saucy drinking song, known as 'The Ballad of Lydia Pinkham', with verses like:

> Peter Whelan, he was sad
> Because he only had one nut
> Till he took some of Lydia's compound
> Now they grow in clusters 'round his butt.

In 1968 a more sanitised version, 'Lily the Pink', proved a massive hit in the UK charts for The Scaffold. By then Lydia Pinkham's company was in terminal decline and even the medicinal compound of the song couldn't save it. With 'Lily the Pink' at number one in the charts, the family finally sold their business.

❧

If there is no such thing as a universal cure, there is, strangely, such a thing as universal symptoms . . .

❧

The stress and the strain

Hungarian endocrinologist Hans Selye has gone down in history as the 'father of stress', perhaps a slightly unfortunate moniker, but one that is apposite in more than one way.

Before 1936 there was no such thing as 'stress' outside the worlds of physics and engineering. It was in that year that Selye wrote a letter to the editor of *Nature*, using the term to describe an effect he had first noted as a medical student in Czechoslovakia in the 1920s.

Coming from four generations of doctors, Selye had always expected to become a physician but during his training his interest had been piqued by an odd observation. The patients he saw in hospital every day all had, by and large, the same general set of symptoms. Whilst he was being told by his tutors that specific diseases cause specific diagnostic indicators, he couldn't help but notice that patients actually shared most of them with everyone else who was ill. It was this thought that would lead him away from the life of a general practitioner and into research.

Selye got his chance to work on his idea in 1936 when he took a research post at McGill University in Montreal, Canada. Here he was tasked with looking for a new placental hormone, which involved the gothic process of grinding up cow ovaries and injecting into live rats the chemicals extracted from the resulting slurry. This, not surprisingly, produced a set of symptoms in the rats that Selye hoped would show the specific action of the mystery hormone. Like any good scientist, he had to check his results, so, as a control, he injected saline into other rats. To his dismay, the same symptoms materialised.

Slowly it dawned on Selye that what he was seeing was not the response to a specific injected agent but a generalised physical response to being repeatedly injected with stuff – any stuff. It was becoming clear that the body had a set of standard responses to attack and he christened this the 'stress response'.

This breakthrough opened up a whole new area of medicine, introducing the study of how environment can put pressure on an organism, creating a response that can in itself over time become damaging – the universal modern condition of 'stress'.

However, the initial stress caused by Selye's work was of an entirely different kind. Selye was a brilliant man, speaking eight languages well and capable of holding a basic conversation in another six, but English, the language of his letter to the editor of *Nature*, was not his mother tongue. He had therefore got a little confused between two English words – 'stress' and 'strain'. The physical term 'stress' referred to a force acting on an object, causing it to deform. 'Strain' was the change wrought in that object by the applied stress. When Salye said 'stress', he meant 'strain'.

Not surprisingly, this caused a degree of strain amongst the medical community now commissioned to translate the new studies into a host of different languages. Everyone knew what he meant by 'stress' – he meant 'strain' – but he had called the response 'stress', despite the polite suggestions of the editor of *Nature* that he might do well to choose a different term. The question arose: should translators use their language's word for 'strain' when describing Selye's 'stress', or should they use the word for 'stress', which wouldn't of course be right?

This issue particularly strained the members of the French Academy charged with protecting the purity of the French language whilst also trying to grapple with what to call a lecture that Selye was about to give to the Collège de France. In the end they decided to invent a new French word – *le stress* – an idea taken up by many other nations equally baffled by the problem.

Indeed, the medical term stress today is one of the few terms that are written in the Roman alphabet even in languages such as Chinese, Arabic and Russian, all of which use a different alphabet. This just leaves English, the source of the problem, where no one can still be quite sure whether they're suffering from stress or strain. As one of Selye's colleagues once put it: 'Stress, in addition to being itself, was also the cause of itself, and the result of itself.'

If stress was a twentieth-century invention, pain was older than medicine itself, yet two of the greatest and most controversial discoveries in treating pain would not occur until the late nineteenth century and then in the space of a fortnight, on one man's workbench.

The agony and the ecstasy

Felix Hoffmann was undoubtedly having a good fortnight. It was August 1897 and, as a research chemist working for Heinrich Dreser at the world's first Big Pharma company, Bayer AG, he had been entrusted with synthesising two experimental drugs.

Neither of these had actually been invented at Bayer, although Dreser would later dispute this, but it was undoubtedly Dreser who saw the opportunity to scale up production and turn them into worldwide wonder drugs.

The first was apparently the least interesting. Hoffmann had taken salicylic acid, an extract of willow bark that was known to have anti-inflammatory effects, and, using a technique pioneered by fellow Bayer researcher Arthur Eichengruen, synthesised from this the substance acetylsalicylic acid. This process made the drug stable and prevented some of the digestive problems associated with the plain salicylic acid. Hoffmann took the results to Dreser, who was unimpressed with them, and went back to his own workbench.

Two weeks later Hoffmann found himself again acetylating, as chemists sometimes do, this time taking opium-derived morphine and from it synthesising diacetylmorphine. This experiment was also initially a bit of a disappointment. Hoffmann and Dreser had hoped that the process would produce codeine, a constituent of opium with fewer unpleasant side effects than morphine. Instead he had just produced an acetylated form of morphine two and a half times more potent than morphine itself.

All was not lost, however. Dreser was one of the first commercial chemists to use extensive drug trials on animals, his staff and himself (see page 97). These showed that diacetylmorphine had a number of very useful properties, most noticeably in calming respiration, soothing coughs and promoting sleep. At the end of the nineteenth century, an era of uncontrolled and almost untreatable respiratory disease, these were all blessings. Coughs were not simply an inconvenience, but, through pneumonia and tuberculosis, for example, they could be killers too.

Dreser determined to take the product to market as a cough cure and looked around for a suitable brand name. Some of his human guinea pigs had noted that the drug made them feel pretty good. One went as far as to say it made him feel 'heroic' or *heroisch* in German. So it seemed only reasonable to call the new drug 'heroin'.

Heroin was a splendid success for Bayer in its early days, notably in the USA where drug enforcement was notoriously light and patent medicines flooded the market. Soon everything from cough pastilles to baby medicines were being laced with the drug, which was said to be non-addictive (unlike morphine) and non-toxic. In Britain the craze for heroin was even more pronounced, with heroin being included as a pick-me-up in hampers for soldiers.

Of course this couldn't last. By the beginning of the twentieth century it was already becoming clear that heroin was, in fact, highly addictive and that, in the USA in particular, a growing group of people was becoming reliant on it as it rapidly took the place of morphine addiction. In 1914 the US prohibited its sale outside of prescription and in 1924 banned its use outright.

In Britain things were a little more lax. Soldiers in the First World War could still get a nip of heroin to help them in the trenches. As late as 1955, *The Times* newspaper was running an editorial on the benefits of the drug, which was finally officially controlled only by the 1971 Misuse of Drugs Act. Indeed, clinical heroin (diamorphine) is still used in UK hospitals, accounting for 95 per cent of the world's legal consumption.

By then Bayer had long moved out of the heroin market, ending production in 1913, but Dreser still had one more trick up his sleeve. The worldwide market for heroin might have collapsed, and the growth of the illegal market in the drug might have caused untold damage to society, but that other drug Hoffmann had synthesised could now at least come into its own.

At first Dreser had not been keen on the acetylsalicylic acid that Hoffmann had produced just two weeks before creating heroin, but in 1899, with news of problems over heroin already reaching the company, he finally agreed to promote it as an analgesic, taking a royalty into the bargain. Again, all he now needed was a name for this wonderful, anti-inflammatory painkiller that didn't irritate the stomach. It would go on to become the most well-known name of any drug and the most widely used drug in history – aspirin.

⁓

If Hoffmann could never have predicted
the uses and abuses of his creations, the effect
of heroin was at least so rapid and pronounced
as to make its nature clear. At the turn of the
century there was another killer at work,
quieter but just as deadly.

⁓

The Radium Girls

Today we view the term 'radioactive' with a degree of suspicion. Now that the effects of ionising radiation are well known, due at least in part to the effects of the unleashing of two nuclear weapons in inhabited cities, radiation is not something we readily welcome into our lives. However, in the years immediately following the discovery of this 'mysterious' phenomenon, this was not always the case, particularly when it came to the wonder substance radium.

Radium had been discovered in 1898 in the uranium ore pitch-blende by Marie Curie and her husband. It was a fascinating element, emitting ionising radiation but also glowing a fetching blue colour in the dark, something that at the time was considered both a novelty and a potential benefit. Of course, anything new was fodder for the quacks and snake-oil salesmen of the day, who decided on the spot that this strange glowing material was clearly a cure-all, suitable for adding to drinks, foods, creams and pills – even toothpaste (see page 55) – in the hope of improving people's lives. It was said to cure a host of dangerous diseases, including, ironically, cancer, and was put in radioactive trusses, hearing aids (sold as 'Hearium') and even condoms.

Most popular of all was Radithor, a radioactive tonic produced by a Harvard drop-out and variously marketed as 'liquid sunshine' and 'a cure for the living dead', although it might more accurately have been described as a cure for living. The deadly effects of the massive dose of radiation in this 'tonic' came to light only after the tragic death of American socialite Eben Byers, who drank nearly 1,400 bottles of the stuff and in the process ingested three times the lethal amount. Far from improving his health, his consumption had led to severe bone and brain abscesses, followed by, not surprisingly, death. In reporting his demise, *The Wall Street Journal* ran the vaguely unsympathetic headline: 'The Radium Water Worked Fine until His Jaw Came Off.'

However, there was also a real, practical, use for radium. As it glowed in the dark, it appeared an ideal material to add to paints used on the dials of instruments in aircraft, which needed to be seen at night yet without blinding the pilot to the view outside the cockpit. Equally it would enable millions of watch owners to tell the time in the dark – which seemed a rather good idea. The catalyst for this was the First World War, which saw the large-scale development of a whole radium industry centred on the US Radium Corporation, whose New Jersey factory was soon employing dozens of young women to paint luminous numbers on the dials of watches.

It was a painstaking job. The paint was a mixture of water, glue and radium powder, which was applied to the dials by hand with a fine camel-hair brush. The cloying nature of the paint meant that the brushes quickly lost their point, smudging the numbers, so the girls were advised to lick the brush between their lips to 'sharpen' it after a few strokes. The result was glowing lips, which the girls thought rather fun. Sometimes they would deliberately paint their lips, nails or even teeth before going out to surprise their friends. One even noticed that in winter when she sneezed, her handkerchief glowed green afterwards.

It was only after the war that any of the girls noticed anything was wrong. One of the painters, Grace Fryer, had left the Radium Corporation in 1920 to take a job as a bank teller, but two years later her teeth began falling out, making her work dealing with the public a shade embarrassing. The situation worsened over the next few years and her doctor ordered X-rays, which showed that she had deep bone abscesses in her jaw. Initially her doctor had no idea what might be the cause, until, in 1925, a colleague suggested that it was perhaps related to her work with radium. Between 1917 and 1920 she had been painting 250 dials a day and estimated that she had licked her brush six times for each dial. Grace, learning that other girls from the factory had health problems, sued the Radium Corporation, although it would take two years for her to find a lawyer prepared to represent her.

Eventually five dial painters, soon known to the press as 'The Radium Girls', took on the corporation, which, as one would expect, denied all wrong-doing. The ensuing case was a media sensation. Managers and scientists at the Radium Corporation were shown to be aware of the dangers and to have taken great care when handling radium themselves, whilst telling their painters that it was harmless. Furthermore they blamed the radiation dose that the girls had received on the X-rays their doctors had taken and outrageously suggested that the bone abscesses were caused by syphilis. By the time the girls appeared at their first court hearing, Grace had lost all her teeth, was unable to walk and could sit up only with the aid of a back brace. Two others were bedridden and none could raise her arm to take the oath.

Central to the case was the testimony of Joseph P. Knef, a

New York dentist who, in 1922, had treated another dial painter, Amelia Maggia, the sister of two of the 'Radium Girls'. He had removed her hugely decayed jawbone shortly before she died and had become concerned that the cause was occupational, despite her death being recorded as from syphilis. Knef had kept the jaw and, as an experiment, wrapped it in dental film, which, when developed, showed the ghostly outline of the jaw, clearly demonstrating that the bone was emitting radiation.

After a year of legal delays instituted by the corporation in the hope that the girls might all die before the case came before a jury, and during which evidence against the corporation mounted, the trial was scheduled for June 1928. Just before it came to court, a federal judge offered to mediate in an out-of-court settlement. The girls, who by this time were dying, agreed to payments of $10,000 and $600 a year for life with all medical bills paid. It was not the $250,000 they had sued for and they realised that the mediating judge was hardly neutral, being a stockholder in the Radium Corporation, but money was time and time was tragically against them. As their lawyer put it: 'When you have heard that you are going to die, that there is no hope – and every newspaper you pick up prints what really amounts to your obituary – there is nothing else.'

The Radium Girls did not die in vain, however. Their sensational case led to new employment laws to protect workers as well as new safety standards for working with radioactive materials. They also left one final gift to future generations. It was from the dial painters that Robley D. Evans made the first clinical measurements on radiation doses, which established safe tolerance levels for radium, so that no one else should suffer the Radium Girls' fate.

5

Domestic Science

(In which we take tea with sweeteners, drink soda pop and beer, and drive around in a bean.)

The cook was a good cook, as cooks go; and as cooks go, she went.

Saki (Hector Hugh Munro), *Reginald* (1904)

It's easy to see science as something divorced from everyday life but in fact it is all around us and nowhere more so than in the kitchen, a veritable hive of physics, chemistry and biology – both wanted and unwanted. So where better to begin a journey into the more practical aspects of science?

The mother of level measures

There are few cooks in the annals of science, which is a great shame, particularly as cookery is about as close as many of us ever get to performing an experiment, even if not always a successful one. Thanks to Fanny Farmer, however, many of us are considerably more successful than we might otherwise be.

Fanny Farmer came from a mid-nineteenth-century US family with what was, for its time, an unusual emphasis on properly educating their daughters. It is uncertain quite where this education would have taken Fanny had things been different, but, as in so many tales of science, it is often unexpected changes that lead to remarkable discoveries. For Fanny that change was the sudden onset of paralysis in her left leg, possibly caused by polio, which stopped her school career in its tracks. She was only sixteen.

Unable to attend school, Fanny was forced to stay at home, helping her mother around the house as best she could. In 1887, after the family had moved to Boston, the situation worsened when Fanny's father, a printer, began to have financial difficulties. Fanny – who had regained some use of her leg by then, although she would always walk with a limp – would now have to pay for her keep, so she took a position as a 'mother's helper' with Mrs Charles Shaw, a prominent Bostonian.

There is no single clear version of what happened to Fanny at Mrs Shaw's but, whatever it was, it had to do with cooking. According to some sources, she proved herself a great cook, earning the admiration of the Shaws' daughter Marcia who asked Fanny to teach her. According to others, she was a terrible cook who failed to get to grips with the recipes of the day, but, either way, the end result was that, with Mrs Shaw's enthusiastic encouragement, Fanny enrolled in the Boston Cooking School.

This institution, established in 1879 by the Women's Education Association of Boston, was an extraordinary place. Its purpose was to educate women who intended to treat homemaking not simply as 'the lot of a woman' but as a profession in itself. As a home of the domestic science revolution, which applied scientific processes and techniques to domestic jobs, it taught not just cookery but diet, hygiene, nutrition, sanitation and the chemical analysis of food. Indeed, one source claimed that in later years Fanny would take away samples of dishes from expensive restaurants to analyse their contents in the lab.

At the Boston Cooking School, Fanny found her forte. After the two-year course she proved so adept that she was kept on as the principal's assistant and in 1891 became principal herself. The qualities that had made her such a success would be revealed to the world five years later only with the publication of her best-selling book *The Boston Cooking School Cook Book*.

Until its publication, most recipes suffered from one alarming deficiency that could easily scupper the good work of any chef: there were no uniform quantities. Some recipes called for a 'lump' of butter or a 'fist' of flour; others referred to cups of water or jugs of milk; various condiments and herbs were measured out in spoons and pinches; but none of these recipe writers bothered to identify precisely how much any of these volumes represented. No one knew how big a 'jug' was as there was no standard 'jug'. It was simply as big as the jug that the recipe writer had to hand and if your jug wasn't the same size – not that you could possibly know whether it was or not – then the recipe was likely to fail.

Fanny Farmer's moment of genius was the realisation that the techniques of science could end this misery once and for all. Fanny treated recipes like chemical experiments. She understood that the quantities needed to be precise and they needed to be standardised. At the Boston Cooking School, she spent months measuring and weighing in various containers, averaging out results, to produce a set of standardised measurements that everyone could follow. She was the first to decide just how much there was in a cup, a teaspoon and a tablespoon, and how many of the one should fit into the other. She was also insistent that, to ensure everyone got the same result, the cups and spoons must be filled only until they are level with the top – never heaped up. For this she became known as 'the mother of level measurements'.

Fanny put her idea to use in her revolutionary recipe book, many of whose recipes were actually taken from the previous principal's own book, but which were now presented with scientific accuracy. It was a revolution that every cook could identify with, the only doubter being her publisher, who decided to print just 3,000 copies and those at Fanny's own expense.

Fanny, however, would have the last laugh. Having published the books at her own cost, she retained all the rights in her work. To date the book has sold over 4 million copies and can claim to be the prototype from which all subsequent, usable recipe books follow.

❧

In millions of kitchens across the world, every day begins with a shot of something to wake us up a bit, yet we rarely hear about the prodigy who first isolated this key ingredient to most of our breakfasts – good old Dr Poison.

❧

Dr Poison's pick-me-up

The discovery of the modern Western world's drug of choice – caffeine – is an unlikely tale involving deadly nightshade, a cat and Germany's most famous poet.

Friedrich Runge was something of a chemical prodigy. Born in 1794 in Billwärder near Hamburg, he spent his teenage years exploring the effects of extract of belladonna (deadly nightshade) on living things – notably himself. In the process he discovered the pupil-dilating effects of the drug atropine in the plant that would later be put to such ghoulish use by Dr Robert Buchanan (see page 245). By 1819, when still only twenty-five years old, Runge was working with the renowned chemist Johann Wolfgang Döbereiner whose work foreshadowed Mendeleev's (see page 84) invention of the Periodic Table of Elements.

Döbereiner was at the height of his powers and his work had come to the attention of an unlikely patron – Johann Wolfgang von Goethe, baron of the German Empire, polymath and the most famous poet in continental Europe. Goethe was a keen amateur scientist at a time when such men of education and money, with time on their hands and a private laboratory at their disposal, could make substantial contributions to the sciences. Goethe himself studied mineralogy, meteorology, botany, biology (particularly animal morphology), pharmacy and chemistry, as well as regularly attending Döbereiner's lectures. It was through these that Goethe came to hear of his assistant and his trick with belladonna. The great poet immediately asked for a demonstration and the petrified Runge was duly summoned.

Runge, or 'Dr Poison' as his fellow students liked to call him, cut a strange figure, marching through the Jena marketplace in borrowed top hat and tailcoat (both of which were de rigueur for a formal visit to Germany's literary colossus), with his apparatus in one hand and his nervous pet cat in the other. At Goethe's house, Runge duly performed his experiment with atropine on his cat, explaining how his accidentally splashing the concoction in his own eye had led him to the discovery. Goethe was impressed, noting in his diary for that day that he had met 'a young chemicus . . . who seems to me to be quite promising'.

Indeed, Goethe was so impressed that he decided to give the young Runge a challenge. In his own youth the poet had been fond of two 'stimulants' – alcohol and coffee – to the point that, aged thirty, having started to feel their more negative effects, he swore to cut right back on both. The active ingredient in wine was obviously already well known, but no one knew precisely what it was in coffee that gave it its 'kick'. Coffee was also still a very expensive commodity, so not something to be experimented on lightly.

Goethe, however, was rich enough and interested enough to want to know the answer. As the young Runge was packing up his equipment, the great man produced a small box from his desk containing rare Arabian mocha beans. Handing it to Runge, he asked him to analyse the contents. So bowled over was Runge by the whole visit that he almost forgot to take his cat away with him, an amused Goethe having to remind him: 'You are forgetting your famulus [familiar].'

Goethe's confidence in the young chemist was not misplaced and later that year Runge returned, bearing a fine white crystalline substance that he had isolated from the beans. It was the reason for coffee's stimulating effects – and he christened it *Kaffein*.

It would prove the start of an illustrious career in which Runge would be credited with creating the first aniline (see page 91) blue dye (cyanol) and being the first to isolate quinine (often misattributed to Pelletier and Caventou). He also pioneered the seminal chemistry technique of paper chromatography and opened up the world of industrial coal tar chemistry.

His reward for this pioneering life was disappointing to say the least. In 1850 the business director of the company Runge worked for, E.E. Cochius, managed to gain control of the firm. Feeling threatened by Runge and his work, he dismissed the scientist just two years later. To add further insult to this injury, on Cochius's death his widow fought a successful legal case to reduce Runge's pension and evict him from the company house that he had been allowed to retain in 'retirement'. Now that Runge was in need of a pick-me-up himself, his friends clubbed together and found him a small house in Oranienburg where he could live out the last ten years of his life.

❧

Traditionally, in Britain Dr Poison's discovery has been taken in the form of tea rather than the coffee preferred in the USA, but it is thanks to a misunderstanding in the USA that we make our tea today in the same way that they do.

❧

Tea bags

The USA has always had an equivocal relationship with tea. America is today seen as a coffee-drinking nation, whilst tea is the symbol of Britain, the old colonial power that the younger country shrugged off with a revolutionary war, started, perhaps not surprisingly, by some tea-inspired vandalism.

Yet the way the British and much of the world drink tea today owes its origins to an entirely accidental American discovery. The process of making tea was, for many decades, extremely time consuming. A pot had to be warmed first, then leaf tea added, followed by boiling water. This had to brew and, when ready, be poured into a cup via a strainer to remove the soaked leaves. Even so, cheaper tea – and the dust produced in packing it – meant that the drink was often a shade 'lumpy'.

Not that any of this bothered Thomas Sullivan, a wholesale tea and coffee merchant operating out of New York in the early twentieth century. What did bother him was giving away something for nothing. As a wholesaler he was expected to provide samples of his tea, traditionally sent out free in tin canisters. This was expensive, both in terms of the quantity of tea and the canisters themselves, so he hit upon a simpler idea. He would package up single-cup quantities of tea in a small silk bag. Prospective buyers would receive just one cup's worth in a disposable bag that they could cut open and try out.

So that's exactly what Sullivan did. What he forgot to do, however, was include any instructions – after all, everyone knew how to make tea and no one needed to be told how to open a bag. Or did they? When puzzled shopkeepers started receiving his silk bags, they assumed that this was a new device for making mess-free tea. The silk bag was obviously meant to be dipped in boiling water in the cup and then just thrown away – no straining, no tea leaves in the sink. It was a brilliant idea and so, much to Sullivan's consternation, they started asking not for bulk orders but for more and more of the little 'tea bags'.

And so, through an accident of packaging, the tea bag was born. Initially the idea was slow to take off, until Sullivan replaced the silk with cheaper and more porous gauze. Then in 1930 a

Boston-based businessman, William Hermanson, invented the heat-sealed paper tea bag, making the bags even cheaper.

In Britain there remained a dogged resistance to this new and easier way of making tea and it was not until 1953 that Joseph Tetley set up his first tea bag factory. Even so, by 1963 only 3 per cent of tea in Britain was sold in bag form. The sea change occurred just one year later with the introduction of the perforated tea bag, which, in Britain at least, seemed to make all the difference. Today 96 per cent of tea in Britain comes in bags – 125 million cups a day. All thanks to an American misunderstanding.

༄

If we're having tea I should probably offer you some sugar. Or perhaps a sweetener?

༄

Eat me

Chemistry can be a dangerous subject and when dealing with novel substances it's always best to carefully follow your instructions. Occasionally, however, the greatest breakthroughs come from doing just the reverse.

Shashikant Phadnis, to be scrupulously fair, had no intention of going against his supervisor's wishes. It was the end of the summer of 1975. The young Indian chemist and Professor Leslie Hough were working together on new applications for an old substance – sucrose – or sugar as we generally call it. Their work at Queen Elizabeth College, which is now part of King's College, London, was centred on creating derivatives of this common molecule and then testing them to see whether they might have industrial applications. In particular they had been adding the rather toxic and corrosive sulfuryl chloride to sucrose, which reacted violently to form the elaborately named 1′,4,6′-trichlorogalactosucrose trichlorosucrose. This substance, in fine powdered form, was sitting on the workbench when a serendipitous misunderstanding took place.

Having isolated this novel substance, Professor Hough asked his student to test it. Shashikant Phadnis misheard his supervisor and thought he had, rather recklessly, been ordered to 'taste' it. With a sense of duty going far beyond what might reasonably be expected of any student, Phadnis picked up a spatula, placed a small amount of the untested white powder on the end and put it to his lips.

At this point it should be reiterated that this is never really a good idea. One of the substances the team were hoping to create by chlorinating sucrose was an insecticide, and tasting insecticides is never to be recommended. But the mistake had been made and Phadnis now tasted the results.

And the results tasted wonderful. It seemed that 1′,4,6′-trichlorogalactosucrose trichlorosucrose was sweet – amazingly sweet; indeed, it would later be found to be around 600 times sweeter than sugar and twice as sweet as saccharine. Phadnis was impressed and relayed this to Professor Hough, causing some consternation: 'When I reported my findings to Les, he asked if I was crazy . . . could I taste compounds without knowing anything about their toxicity?' It was a very good point and obviously many more tests would need to be carried out, but this serendipitous discovery would lead the team in a whole new direction.

Initially the substance needed a name and, considering the surprising route that had led to its discovery, Hough and Phadnis settled provisionally on 'serendipitose'. This was in the great tradition of giving tongue-in-cheek provisional names to newly discovered substances. When Albert Szent-Gyorgyi first isolated ascorbic acid and published his findings, he called the new substance 'ignose' since he was convinced it was a sugar that resembled glucose and fructose, but remained ignorant of its structure. When the editor of the *Biochemical Journal* refused to accept this as a sensible name, Szent-Gyorgyi suggested 'Godnose' instead.

Next the pair made contact with sugar manufacturer Tate & Lyle and spent the following year testing various chlorinated sugars to find that Holy Grail of food manufacturing – a zero-calorie, safe sweetener. In 1991, Canada finally became the first country to approve 1',4,6'-trichlorogalactosucrose trichloro-sucrose, or sucralose as it was now known, for human consumption. Shashikant Phadnis's potentially lethal misunderstanding had reached the sweetest of endings.

∾

Just as chemists have been to work on our tea and sweeteners, so they've even had a go at the butter on our toast. Well, not exactly butter . . .

∾

I can believe it's not butter

In 1869, France was not the happiest of places to be, as the country was in the grip of a depression and war was looming with Prussia, so perhaps not surprisingly, the French emperor Napoleon III found himself pondering a number of tricky problems. One of these involved butter.

France, like most Western European countries, had seen a rapid shift in population from the countryside to the new industrial towns and with it had come both a reduction in the production of milk and an increase in demand. The depression had further made all milk products, and especially butter, very expensive and, as French rulers knew, the lack of staple foods could make their population a touch jumpy. As it also looked as if the emperor would have to find food for a large army and navy in the coming war, something had to be done.

Napoleon III's answer was a competition. In a decree he announced a substantial prize for the first person to create 'a suitable substance to replace butter for the navy and the less prosperous classes'.

In all honesty the competition was not perhaps as successful as Napoleon would have hoped, there being only one entrant. Fortunately, Hippolyte Mège-Mouriez would prove a worthy winner. A chemist with a particular interest in food, he had already come to the attention of the emperor, thanks to his technique for improving bread yield in army kitchens, and the invention of a healthier chocolate, work that had gained him two gold medals and the Légion d'Honneur. Given the facilities of the emperor's private farm, the Ferme Impériale de la Faisanderie in Vincennes, he turned his attention to butter substitutes.

Mège-Mouriez's first observation – that the milk from under-nourished cows was not significantly lower in fat than that of well-fed animals – led him to believe that cows turned body fat into milk fat in the stomach or possibly in the udder, a conclusion that is absolutely wrong but paradoxically led him in the right direction.

He began his experiments making artificial butter by, bizarrely, taking chopped beef suet and mixing it with warm water and minced sheep stomach. Adding chemicals to suppress the acidity, he found that after a few hours the enzymes in the minced stomach had digested the fibrous parts of the suet, leaving fat floating clear on the surface of the water. This, as he understood it, was how cows made milk fat – by breaking down body fat in their stomachs, and so he assumed the oily product floating on the water was actually butter. He couldn't have been more wrong as he discovered when he tasted the substance.

Mège-Mouriez had made fat but he was having no trouble in believing that it wasn't butter. In an attempt to make the substance more 'buttery', he rather unpleasantly tried adding some chopped udder, along with sodium bicarbonate and, most importantly of all, milk. The result was something that, whilst certainly not butter, had a similar fat content and was a lot cheaper. The only real drawback was its colour – a pearly white. It was probably this (or possibly margaric acid) that led him to call his invention 'oleomargarine', *márgaron* being Greek for 'pearl' and oleo oil being the name given to soft beef fat.

Oleomargarine, later contracted to 'margarine', went on to win the competition and, at half the price of butter, looked likely to take the market by storm. Napoleon gave Mège-Mouriez a generous prize and a factory was established to produce the new wonder food. Sadly for Mège-Mouriez, the events of the Franco-Prussian War rather overtook margarine and he failed to make the fortune he might have expected from the discovery. In 1871 he sold his patent to the Dutch company Jurgens.

Margarine went on to have a chequered history. Its cheapness proved a direct threat to dairy farmers and across the world governments were soon being lobbied to impose higher taxes on the product or find other ways to protect butter sales. In particular the unfortunate colour that gave margarine its name was exploited, with many countries instituting laws to prevent the addition of yellow colouring to make the substance look more palatable. In response, some margarine manufacturers began selling white margarine with attached yellow food-colour capsules for the consumer to mix in themselves. Attempts were even made in some US states to force manufacturers to dye the product pink to make it even less appetising, whilst in others it was banned outright. In Wisconsin the absolute ban on margarine was lifted only in 1967.

∽

If the margarine is a bit peculiar, perhaps you'd
like a fizzy drink to take the taste away?

∽

Dr Nooth's apparatus

A sideboard is an unlikely place to find a piece of laboratory
equipment but there was a time, in the eighteenth century,
when every fashionable English dining room sported just such
a device, the gift to the world of the researches of Joseph Priestley
(see page 12) and the ingenuity of Dr John Nooth.

The precise details of this apparatus could be found in the
work of Priestley who, living next door to a brewery, had an
almost limitless supply of what he called 'fixed air' and which
we know as carbon dioxide. 'Fixed air' had first been identified
by the Scottish physician Joseph Black, but it was Priestley who
had discovered that he could manufacture the gas by dripping
sulphuric acid on to marble (calcium carbonate) and then
dissolve the gas in water.

Dissolving carbon dioxide in water was important to Priestley.
The process created soda water and is the basis of all modern
'fizzy' drinks but Priestley believed it had a higher purpose.
This was the age of the great spas and the taking of naturally
occurring sparkling mineral waters had become a health craze.
Priestley himself believed (erroneously) that his soda water
might help prevent scurvy and in 1772 published a paper,
Directions for Impregnating Water with Fixed Air, which he
hoped would provide naval captains with a means of making
soda water for the crew when away at sea for long periods.
Indeed, the instructions were taken by Captain Cook on his
second voyage.

So keen was Priestley on the production of soda water that he created his own simple apparatus for making it, utilising only readily available components that he hoped any keen amateur would be able to obtain. His machine consisted of a glass bottle in which marble and sulphuric acid were reacted, which was, in turn, attached to a pig's bladder that collected the resultant gas. The bladder was attached to another tube, which, when the bladder was squeezed, delivered the gas to a water-filled bottle sitting inverted in a tray of water. Some of the gas dissolved in the water as it bubbled into the bottle, making a mildly sparkling drink. Not exactly the 'real thing' but a start.

It was this apparatus that came to the attention of Scottish physician John Nooth. He too was interested in the health-giving properties of soda water but felt that there was one thing holding it back from universal acceptance, and that was Priestley's machine. Nooth claimed that the apparatus was too complicated and suitable only for experts to use. Worse still, he said it imparted the flavour of urine to the drink, thanks to the pig's bladder. Finally, noting that the idea of dissolving carbon dioxide in water was not unique to Priestley anyway, he came up with his own bladderless apparatus as a rival. This consisted of a glass soda fountain made from three chambers, one on top of the other. In the bottom chamber, chalk and acid were mixed to produce gas, which passed through a valve into the middle chamber containing the water. The top chamber contained another reservoir of water, which kept the gas and water in the middle chamber under pressure and provided an overflow system.

Perhaps not unreasonably, Priestley was rather put out by the claim that his soda water tasted of urine. He denounced Nooth, claiming his pigs' bladders had never tainted the water and, if Nooth had found that to be the case, it must be because one of his servants had urinated in the water before giving it to him, as a trick. This, Priestley hinted, was no more than Nooth deserved.

As one of the great pioneers of public science he also furiously denied the claims that his machine was difficult to use, pointing out that, unlike Nooth's bespoke apparatus, it used 'no other vessels but such as are in constant family use'. What hurt Priestley most, however, was the claim that he was not the true inventor of soda water. He announced he was quite happy to forgo any financial reward for his invention but insisted on having 'the sole merit of the discovery'.

In fact, even Priestley eventually admitted that the Nooth apparatus, being all of one part, was easier to use. Certainly those wealthy enough to afford this delicate piece of glassware agreed, with over 1,000 sets selling in its first three years on the market. Under the name 'gasogene', the Nooth apparatus became a regular feature in the dining rooms of the well-to-do and, in most cases, was the only piece of scientific equipment in the house.

However, his hopes for huge profits, as well as Priestley's desires to see a soda fountain in every home, were soon dashed. In 1792, John Jacob Schweppe, a Swiss watchmaker, moved to London with his new, industrial-scale, high-pressure carbonation process, which provided ready-carbonated drinks, removing the need for families to fiddle around with chalk and highly corrosive acids in their homes. From now on the London elite would buy their drinks ready-fizzed.

❦

Of course the drink of choice for any sane
adult would be beer and, as we've seen, it was a
scientist, Louis Pasteur, who ensured that our
beer was fit to drink. Indeed, so famous did
nineteenth-century scientists become in testing
and improving our food and drink that
Germany's most celebrated chemist was
paid £10,000 just to drink a bottle of ale.

❦

Liebig drinks a beer

Justus von Liebig was a giant in the world of nineteenth-century chemistry, the father of modern laboratory technique, the discoverer of nitrogen (and its role as a plant fertiliser) and, more surprisingly, the founding father of the Oxo stock cube company. Still more oddly, the Liebig condenser, a piece of apparatus known to every chemistry student, is one of the few pieces of equipment that he didn't invent.

By 1845, Liebig was perhaps the most famous scientist in Europe, a baron of the German Empire, and founder and editor of Germany's leading chemistry journal. So it appears reasonable enough that he seemed like a good man to call when the beer brewers of Burton in England developed a public relations problem.

The trouble had begun in 1852 when a French chemist named Payen had commented on the large quantity of the deadly poison strychnine being imported by the British. He suggested, somewhat scurrilously, that the reason for this was that beer brewers of Burton on Trent were using the famously bitter substance in their beer instead of more expensive hops.

The idea was, of course, nonsense. In the first instance, hops were readily and cheaply available; furthermore, strychnine has a distinctively metallic and persistent taste clearly distinguishable from hops; and third, there was a quick and easy chemical test for strychnine that would give the game away. It should also go without saying that it would take a very desperate drinks manufacturer to knowingly put a deadly poison in their best-selling product. In truth, strychnine was imported for one very simple reason – to kill the rats that were making the warehouses of Britain's new industrial heartland their own.

However, rumours persisted and the Allsopp brewery was forced into action. Their first move was to employ two leading chemists, Thomas Graham and August Wilhelm von Hofmann (see page 89), to analyse samples of their pale ales. They conclusively proved that the rumour was false. Hofmann, a friend of Liebig's, thought that perhaps a word from the great man himself might help to calm nerves so he suggested to Allsopp's that Liebig be sent a case and asked to test it further.

The deal was done and in return for £100 (around £10,000 by today's standards) the world's greatest chemist promised to analyse the pale ale. Of course, Liebig had no intention of really doing this. He knew perfectly well that the idea of strychnine adulteration was preposterous and that his friend Hofmann's analysis would need no second opinion. He later wrote to Hofmann of his 'work' on the beer: 'The main test consisted in my drinking a bottle with great enjoyment.'

What Allsopp did get for their £100 was a gushing letter from Liebig which ended: 'I am myself an admirer of this beverage, and my own experience enables me to recommend it, in accordance with the opinion of the most eminent English physicians, as a very agreeable and efficient tonic, and as a general beverage both for the invalid and the robust.'

Soon this ringing scientific endorsement was making its way on to Allsopp's billboards and bottles, forcing their main rival

Bass to also write to Liebig, asking him to analyse *their* beer. For an undisclosed sum he agreed and wrote them a letter too. And so the free beer tasting and fee taking went on . . .

❧

If food has piqued the interest of scientists,
it has not always been for the most obvious of
reasons. To a chemist a bean is not a dinner but
a package of chemicals. To Henry Ford it
was a potential car.

❧

Henry Ford's bean car

Henry Ford has been called many things but rarely 'ecologically friendly', yet were it not for the outbreak of the Second World War we might all, thanks to him, now be driving around in cars made partly from beans.

Ford had an extraordinary interest in soya beans. Having been brought up on a farm, he was a firm believer that crops commonly grown simply for food could be found new industrial uses. By the 1930s he had established a large research team to look into the most promising of these crops – soya. Three things interested Ford in soya: the oil, the fibrous protein that could be extracted from it, and the possibility that its nitrogen-fixing roots could help restore soils devastated by the depression-era 'Dust Bowl'.

However, Henry Ford didn't make beans, he made cars, so his love of soya took him beyond thoughts of farming and into how the humble bean could be used in the automobile revolution. The oil had obvious uses and was added to the enamel paint that was just then beginning to replace the labour-intensive seven coats of hand-finished lacquer that his car bodies had previously sported. By 1935 some 1 million gallons of soya oil were going into this alone. Then there were the shock-absorbers, filled with glycerine derived from soya – another 540,000 gallons per year. A further 200,000 gallons were used in the foundry as a binder for the sand needed in castings. By the late 1930s, the factory in Dearborn, Indiana, required 78,000 acres of soya beans a year to make Ford cars.

What interested Ford more than the oil was the fibrous protein left behind when the beans had been defatted. This, it was discovered, could be mixed with formaldehyde and phenol to make a plastic, enabling the company to 'grow' their own gear-stick knobs, electrical buttons, glove compartment doors and even tractor seats. Even more impressive was the fact that the plastic didn't need to be painted as it could be dyed right through and polished to a high finish.

Yet even this was not enough for Ford. As he commented in 1934: 'Someday you and I will see the day when auto bodies will be grown down on the farm.' As Ford was not a man to wait for others to fulfil his predictions, he fulfilled it himself with the introduction of the first soya bean plastic car.

From the late 1930s, Ford's team of chemists had been working on producing car panels from soya plastic, which they hoped would be both lighter and more resilient than sheet steel, making cars more efficient and stronger. In 1940 a soya lid was attached to the boot (or trunk) of one of Ford's own cars and in November of that year he arranged one of his famous publicity stunts to announce it to the world. Inviting the press to see his car, Ford, then aged seventy-seven, suddenly produced an axe, its blade covered, and proceeded to slam the back of the axehead into the boot. The axe bounced off, greatly impressing the gentlemen of the press. He then asked the gathered pressmen whether any of them would dare to perform the same act on the steel boots of their own cars. All politely refused.

The following year, on 13 August 1941, at his local community festival, Ford revealed a car made entirely with plastic panels, made from cellulose and resin pressed into cloth. Unlike Bakelite and the other plastics of the day, this took a high shine like painted steel, would not rust, and when deformed would flex but not bend. It was also half the weight of steel. To celebrate, Ford invited the pressmen to join him in a fourteen-course lunch, consisting wholly of soya-based foods. In the general merriment it was quickly forgotten (if it was ever mentioned) that these plastic panels actually contained very little soya, as Ford's engineers had had trouble making the substance fully waterproof, despite Ford's own belief in the miracle bean.

Ford himself lost none of his personal enthusiasm, however, having a suit made of 30 per cent soya fibre and 70 per cent wool, to match a tie made of the same fabric. His chief soya scientist, Robert A. Boyer, even made his own wife a soya coat, a process that also gave Boyer the idea of 'knitting' textured soya protein into meat substitutes.

By this time the war was taking its toll on bean research. The pilot plant built to make soya protein fibre was converted to producing aircraft engines and by the end of the war petro-chemical-derived plastics were proving themselves more versatile and cheaper than soya ones. By the time Henry Ford died in 1947, he had spent over $4 million on soya research but in an era when few, including Ford, worried about the supply or side effects of using fossil fuels, the soya bean car was quickly forgotten.

∞

With all this biology and chemistry
you're probably wondering whether there's a
place for any physics in this eccentric kitchen.
Of course there is. That's how we're going
to cook dinner – with radar.

∞

Ready in one minute

By 1941, Percy LeBron Spencer was already a hero. As an engineer at the Raytheon Company he had been charged with turning a complex but vital new instrument, invented by two British scientists, into a mass-produced tool. The object in question was the cavity magnetron, a device at the heart of the new radar technology.

The problem Spencer had was that each magnetron had to be carved out of a solid copper block to a tolerance of less than one 10,000th of an inch. The best machinists in the country had been employed and in great numbers, but this had merely lifted production from one a week to seventeen per day. Spencer's genius had been to remove the machining altogether and build the magnetrons in machine-punched slices, glued together with silver solder. This work could be done by an unskilled workman to the same tolerance as the old machined devices. Now Raytheon was producing 2,600 magnetrons a day.

It was an astonishing achievement for a largely self-taught and twice-orphaned boy who had started work aged just twelve. But it was not to be his major claim to fame. Spencer continued to work with magnetrons, making various improvements to radar design that would win him the Distinguished Public Service Award – the highest honour the US Navy can give a civilian – yet it was only after the war that he shot to fame.

Spencer was examining a working magnetron in a Raytheon laboratory in 1946 when he noticed that the peanut bar in his pocket was getting hot. This peculiar effect had previously been noted by other scientists when working with magnetrons and no one had felt the need to investigate further. Spencer, however, the perennial inquisitive child, was different. He sent out for some popping corn and, sure enough, when he placed it near the magnetron it began popping all over the lab.

Spencer reasoned that the microwave energy must be heating the corn so he decided to experiment. The next day he came to the office with an old kettle and cut a hole in the side of it before placing the hole against a magnetron. He then placed a raw egg in the kettle and switched on the magnetron. Nothing happened. One of his fellow engineers went to investigate, just in time to get a faceful of very hot scrambled egg.

Spencer had discovered that it was possible to cook with the microwave radiation from a magnetron. Not only that, instead of slowly heating food from the outside – a time-consuming and energy-intensive operation – microwaves excited water molecules throughout a food in a matter of seconds.

Initial success with microwave cooking was limited as the 1947 'RadarRanges', as Spencer christened them, were 6 feet high, needed to have a plumbed-in cooling system and cost the equivalent of $50,000. Indeed, it would be 1967 before Raytheon produced a table-top model for the home. Just eight years later, however, sales of microwave ovens in the US began to outstrip the sale of gas ranges and mealtimes began to be announced not with a gong but with a 'ping'.

∽

And finally we shouldn't forget the humblest
but perhaps the most ubiquitous contribution of
science to the average kitchen – the bag in
which we brought the food home.

∽

Paper bags

Margaret Knight was one of those people who, when they see
a problem, are determined to come up with a solution. This
principle was first forcefully brought home to her in 1850 when,
aged just twelve, she witnessed an accident.

Knight's early years had not been easy. Her father had died
when she was still very young, leaving the family with no money.
They had been forced to move from their original home in York,
Maine, to Manchester, New Hampshire, where her education
was cut short in favour of her taking a paying job in a mill. It
was here that she had witnessed a steel-tipped shuttle fly off a
loom when its thread broke, badly injuring a workman. Despite
her youth and lack of formal education, she had immediately
set about solving the dilemma of flying shuttles and had soon
created a safety device for the looms. Thanks to her decision
not to patent the device, it was soon in use across Manchester.

This, however, was only a taste of things to come. At the end
of the US Civil War, Knight moved to Springfield, Massachusetts,
where she found manual work with the Columbia Paper Bag
Company. Making paper bags is perhaps not the most inspiring
of jobs but it did get the ever-resourceful Knight thinking. The
standard bag produced at the factory was simply a cylinder of
paper sealed at one end but Knight noted that it was in fact a
very poor way of carrying anything that wasn't flat. What was

really needed for things like groceries and everyday shopping was a paper bag with a flat bottom that could stand upright and be evenly loaded without forcing the base apart. Of course, such box-folded bags were possible but they had to be made by hand, flying in the face of the main point of paper bags, which was to be cheap.

So, despite having no formal mechanical training, Margaret Knight set to work studying the folding patterns of the flat-bottomed bag and devising a machine that could fold and glue them. Her initial model was made in her apartment from wood but the bosses of the Columbia factory were so impressed that they persuaded her to take the design to a Boston machine shop to have a working steel version made. The following year she applied for what would be only the second patent ever granted an American woman.

It must have come as something of a shock to her when her application was refused on the grounds that a near-identical patent had only recently been granted to one Charles Annan. It turned out that Annan had spent a lot of time over the previous year at the Boston machine shop where he had seen Knight's model and clearly had just copied her design. Knight immediately sued for patent interference, a bold move at a date when a man could claim that simply being a man made an invention more likely to be his, as a woman could hardly be expected to achieve such a thing. That is exactly what Annan claimed but thanks to a string of witnesses, including managers at the Columbia factory and Knight's landlady who testified to her hours spent on the wooden model, Knight won the day.

With her patent secure, Knight could finally enjoy the fruits of her labours. In Hartford, Connecticut, she founded the Eastern Paper Bag Company, which provided her with an income that allowed her to turn her skills to full-time inventing. In the meantime her flat-bottomed bags became ubiquitous on both sides of the Atlantic, Knight even being decorated by Queen Victoria for her invention. A further twenty-five (some sources say twenty-nine) patents followed, covering everything from sash-frame mechanisms to improvements in rotary engines.

At her death, aged seventy-six in 1913, the *New York Times* characterised her as still working twenty hours a day on what they claimed was her eighty-ninth invention. Her first bag-folding machine is now in the Smithsonian, but her real legacy is on the counter of millions of shops across the world.

6

An Eye for Invention

(In which we watch things stick together, fall
off and walk down the stairs.)

What is the use of a new-born child?

> Benjamin Franklin (when asked what was the use
> of a new invention), in J. Parton,
> *Life and Times of Benjamin Franklin* (1864)

Science is not only about theory or even
cookery, it is about application and some of
the most ubiquitous of applications
have the strangest roots.

⊷

Slot machines

Hero of Alexandria (see page 294) must surely go down in
history as the most underrated boffin of all time. In a later age
his inventions would have been considered world-changing – he
had, after all, invented the steam turbine over 1,800 years before
Sir Charles Parsons got all the credit for doing the exact same
thing.

But that wasn't Hero's only work of genius. Hero was a
wonder worker and what could be more beguiling or confounding
than that mainstay of modern life – the slot machine?

Hero received many of his commissions from temples where
priests thought that a bit of 'magic' might help drum up some
business. In his book on pneumatics, Hero describes how he
started off by inventing the automatic door to entice the
worshipper in.

As the priest and congregation approached they would be
faced with the looming doors of the temple, tightly shut. The
priest would then light a fire on an altar outside and, magically, as though the god was pleased with the offering, the doors
would swing open of their own accord, accompanied by a
fanfare of trumpets. Behind the scenes, where only Hero and
the priests ever went, a complex series of air- and water-filled
tubes connected the altar to large bucket counterweights
attached to the temple doors by pulleys. As the fire heated

the air it expanded, forcing water in another tube into the buckets, which would open the doors when there was enough weight of water in them to set the pulley train in motion. When the fire was extinguished, the air in the pipes cooled and sucked the water back out of the buckets. As the weight in the buckets lessened, so the doors slowly closed under their own weight. It looked like magic but Hero knew it was just hydraulics.

With the thoroughly impressed congregation now inside, Hero suggested a whole host of mechanisms to further dazzle them, including a steam boiler that created a jet of invisible steam on which a ball floated, apparently defying gravity, and a machine where a group of mechanical songbirds sang in a tree until a mechanical owl turned round to stare at them at which they fell silent in terror. There were also steam-powered statues that blinked and waved like exotic extras in a Ray Harryhausen movie and, the standard fare of every modern gardening catalogue, the solar-operated fountain, or, as he put it: 'A Fountain which trickles by the Action of the Sun's Rays.'

This was all well and good but it didn't come cheap and priests buying into such schemes would need to get a return on their money. And that is where Hero played his master stroke. Worshippers entering a temple needed to ritually purify themselves with holy water but collecting the money and dispensing the water was a time-consuming and, frankly, boring job, taking one of the priests away from his other duties. So Hero invented the slot machine to do it for them.

Here then, in the *Treatise on Pneumatics*, is his description of 'Machine 21', the prototype of one of the most loved and hated devices in the modern world, a machine we all regularly use, abuse, kick, hit and swear we will never put money in again: 'Sacrificial Vessel which flows only when Money is introduced. If into certain sacrificial vessels a coin of five drachms be thrown, water shall flow out and surround them. Let ABCD (fig. 21) be a sacrificial vessel or treasure chest, having an opening in its mouth . . .'

But before we condemn Hero for all those chocolate bars that the descendants of his machine have never delivered, he did also modify the mechanism to solve one of the greatest conundrums facing any partygoer.

Parties were just as important a part of ancient life as they are today and then, just as now, it was customary to bring with you something to drink to help break the ice. In Hero's world, that 'something' was wine, and it presented a problem that has remained unchanged for centuries: how do you make sure that other people don't drink all the good stuff you were kind enough to bring, leaving you with the dregs?

Hero's solution was to adapt his holy water dispenser to become an automatic wine dispenser. Guests simply poured their wine into one of several compartments in the machine and took a special counter associated with that compartment. When they wanted a drink, they placed their counter on the dispenser and the weight moved a valve around to release their wine and no one else's.

This, had it caught on, might have gone some way to justifying the creation of one of the world's most infuriating machines. As Hero himself put it in the introduction to his book, he simply hoped his machines would serve two purposes: 'some of which supply the most pressing wants of human life, while others produce amazement and alarm'.

It is still a matter of debate, however, some 1,900 years after Hero's death, whether the slot machine counts as a 'pressing want' or merely produces 'alarm'.

∽

If slot machines weren't what you were expecting in first-century Egypt, then our first piece of information technology might come as even more of a shock – particularly as it was made of the most improbable material.

∽

The worldwide wooden web

There is just far too much to read. This was already an issue in the Middle Ages and it has got exponentially bigger ever since.

For centuries librarians have tried to find ways of cataloguing information to make it accessible and 'cross-referenceable', if that's a word, which it probably isn't, with varying degrees of success. But it has only been in the modern era, with the invention of the worldwide web, that we have for the first time had the ability to scan and compare huge numbers of texts quickly and accurately and, thanks to hypertext, jump between them. The worldwide web, we are told, is the miracle of the modern information age, putting all human knowledge at our fingertips. Whilst I would never wish to diminish the role played by its inventors, the truth is that their miracle was first invented 400 years earlier. And it was made of wood.

To find the real origins of the web we have to delve into an extraordinary book with an extraordinary title: *The Diverse and Artifactitious Machines of Captain Agostino Ramelli*. Ramelli was born in 1531 on the borders of Switzerland and the Duchy of Milan. He makes his first appearance on the historical stage in 1572 as a military engineer in the service of Henri, Duke of Anjou, later king of France.

Under the king's patronage he would write his magnum opus, perhaps the finest example of a whole new genre of literature appearing in the sixteenth century, known as the *Theatrum Machinarum* or 'Theatre of Machines'. They were the engineering equivalent of Chippendale's directory of furniture, offering page after page of mouth-watering designs to appeal to every despot, benevolent dictator and tyrant who had the money for them.

For the more belligerent there were huge catapults, machines for filling in castle ditches, devices for scaling sheer walls, bolt cutters for snipping through portcullises and portable bridges for the army on the move. For those whose martial ambition stopped short of all-out siege warfare, there were tools for removing doors from their hinges or tearing away the bolts that held them shut, which might have appealed more to the jealous lover or cat burglar.

Ramelli, however, was no one-trick wonder. In order to attract the less warlike leaders of his era, interleaved with the machines for lifting artillery into mountainous places, we find intricate illustrations of water pumps, earth excavators and coffer dams, some of which look remarkably similar to some of Leonardo da Vinci's sketches, suggesting that he had at some point had a peek in the great man's notebook.

And it is amongst these extraordinary machines that we find the first worldwide web, the first machine allowing an individual to scan through and compare huge amounts of material, flicking backwards and forwards between texts like one of those people whom information technology pioneer Vannevar Bush would later call 'trail blazers, those who find delight in the task of establishing useful trails through the enormous mass of the common record'.

The first thing that strikes one about Ramelli's worldwide web is the material used to construct it – wood. The information available in his day came not in electronic form but in large, leather-bound books, so accessing lots of it at once required a serious piece of physical engineering. On initial inspection it looks like a waterwheel but each vane has been replaced by a reading desk. Each desk is attached to an epicyclic gearing system, meaning that, as the wheel is turned by the operator searching for a new text, each book remains on its desk without tumbling off.

The idea behind the contraption was to allow the avid researcher – and few were more avid than Ramelli – to read numerous books at once, finding a passage in one and then rotating the wheel to another to cross-reference. It was, to be fair, a rather cumbersome contrivance, whose epicyclic gearing was more about showing potential customers that he knew how epicyclic gears worked than about making a practical machine. Indeed, the device could equally well operate using weights, allowing gravity to keep each desk upright – but, in its own peculiar way, it marked a revolution. The ability to read many texts at once and jump between them was a novelty and Ramelli's machine might be claimed an even more distant predecessor of hypertext than Vannevar Bush's Memex machine.

So if the purpose of the worldwide web is to make the knowledge of the world easily searchable and comparable, its first iteration, or at least its first search engine, was one of Captain Agostino Ramelli's Diverse and Artifactitious Machines.

༄

It is often people from non-scientific careers
who find the right application for a scientific
breakthrough. This can make it harder to gain
recognition for your achievement, particularly
when you're a cheesemonger.

༄

Inventing the telegraph

Francis Ronalds was one of those affable and diligent gentlemen
scientists of the nineteenth century whose good intentions and
open manner were almost certain to leave him largely unrecog-
nised in a subject he helped to invent (see page 298).

Ronalds had started out in business in 1803 as a wholesale
cheesemonger but his real interest lay in the new and exciting
world of electricity. In particular he was fascinated by the trans-
mission of electricity down wires, seeming to travel almost
instantaneously. Now a signal travelling over a large distance in
a very short time might have some practical application, or so
Ronalds thought, especially if that signal carried a message.

Being a practical sort of cheesemonger, Ronalds decided to
try out his theory, in his garden at what would later be known
as Kelmscott House in Hammersmith (at one time the home of
William Morris). Here, beginning in 1814, he built two large
wooden frames, 20 yards apart, and between them strung
8 miles of continuous wire, looped back and forth hundreds
of times and attached to the frames by insulating silken cords.
At each end he attached a device called a 'Canton's Pith Ball
electrometer', which consisted of two pith balls hanging next
to each other on silk threads suspended from the wire. When
electricity travelled down the wire, the pith balls became

similarly charged and repelled each other, moving slightly apart.

He now proceeded to discharge a Leyden jar – an early form of battery – through the wire and, just as he had hoped, noticed that the pith balls deflected at almost the same instant, despite the 8 miles of wire between them.

This seemed promising so, at his own expense, he decided to continue his experiments, this time trying to send a message down the wire. For this test he insulated a 524-foot wire inside glass tubes, which he buried in a wood-lined trench in the garden. A continuous electrical current was sent down the wire using a frictional electrical machine and at each end he attached a clockwork mechanism of his own invention, which, via a brass dial, could indicate the letters of the alphabet.

It was, to be fair, a slow system, although Ronalds did his best to speed it up as much as he could. He was delighted with the result and, putting aside any thoughts of personal profit, refused to take up a patent, offering the machine instead to the British Admiralty. It was, after all, a machine that might transform communication.

Ronalds imagined a time when telegraph offices might spread across the country: 'why should not our kings hold councils at Brighton with their ministers in London? Why should not our government govern at Portsmouth almost as promptly as in Downing Street? Why should our defaulters escape by default of our foggy climate? [. . .] Let us have electrical conversazione offices, communicating with each other all over the kingdom, if we can.'

If Ronalds had hoped for a similar level of enthusiasm at the Admiralty, he was in for a shock. They used semaphore for long-distance communication and considered that to be plenty good enough. Ronalds pointed out that visual semaphore did have a few tiny drawbacks, such as not working at night, or when there was anything in the way, or if it was foggy, but the Lords of the Admiralty were adamant, their secretary, Mr Barrow, writing back in no uncertain terms: 'telegraphs of any kind are now wholly unnecessary.'

And so the first electrical telegraph died a death. Although Ronalds refused to be downhearted, he moved on to other subjects of study. Fortunately the idea was not wholly lost. Amongst the admiring spectators at Ronalds' demonstrations of telegraphy in his garden had been a fourteen-year-old boy who was enthused by what he saw. He was Charles Wheatstone (see page 51) and in 1837 he and his partner William Cooke patented the world's first commercial electrical telegraph. In 1870, in a world now changed almost beyond recognition by the telegraph, Prime Minister William Gladstone finally gave the now eighty-two year old Ronalds the credit he deserved and he was knighted on 31 March.

∽

Once science becomes industrial, it becomes valuable, which means that the ethos of the free dissemination of information that we hope for in the scientific community goes out of the window. But secrecy doesn't always work in your favour.

∽

Hancock's pickle

In the early 1800s rubber was a new and exciting material with lots of potential uses but also a number of drawbacks. For one thing, it was expensive and difficult to work with, leading to wastage but, more annoyingly, it became unworkable if it got too hot or too cold. In extremely cold conditions it became hard and brittle, losing its elasticity, and in exceptional heat it became soft and sticky.

All these complications were well known to Thomas Hancock, a young coachbuilder in London whose interest in the substance was prompted not by a notion as ahead of its time as tyres (although his name would be forever associated with Goodyear's) but by a gratifying concern for his passengers and their luggage. Hancock's early experiments with raw pará rubber focused on applying it to clothing to make it more elastic as well as waterproof, but his technique of applying thin strips of raw rubber to clothes led to costly waste.

Whilst cutting the rubber, however, he noticed that if he immediately put two freshly cut surfaces back together, they stuck, which gave him an idea. Being of a practical frame of mind, he built a machine consisting of a toothed roller that chewed up the waste rubber into hundreds of tiny bits and then re-formed it into a pliable mass. In addition to saving on rubber, Hancock quickly found that the worked rubber produced by his machine was much easier to use and much more easily dissolved in solvents – to make the sort of rubber solution that might go into waterproof clothing.

Of course such a breakthrough was likely to attract imitators, but Hancock seemed unwilling to take out a patent on his device, or 'masticator' as he called it. Instead he swore his workforce to utmost secrecy and insisted that the machine was only ever referred to as his 'pickle', the term, as he put it, being enough to throw anyone off the scent.

Hancock's pickle was a great success and he soon went into the waterproof clothing business, taking a licence from the other great name in rubber clothing, Charles Macintosh, who had patented a method for sandwiching rubber between two layers of cloth. In fact, Hancock's masticated rubber proved so superior to Macintosh's own that from 1830 Hancock supplied the rubber to Macintosh, later becoming a partner in that most famous of all waterproofing businesses, contributing to the partnership both his pickle and an automatic rubber solution spreader.

One problem with rubber remained unresolved, however: its stickiness in heat and its loss of elasticity in low temperatures. And this is where the story becomes a little more murky. In 1842, Stephen Moulton arrived in England with some small samples of 'cured' rubber that had been made in America by Charles Goodyear, using a secret process. This rubber did not get sticky, nor did it go hard when cold, but despite this amazing break-through Goodyear was having trouble finding US backers. Moulton, acting as his agent, was therefore looking to sell the still-unpatented process in Europe. Not surprisingly, Moulton knocked on the door of Charles Macintosh and Company and from there one of the samples came into the hands of a director, William Brockendon, who in turn passed it on to Hancock.

This is the last point on which all sides agree. According to Hancock, the sample he received was of a very poor quality, showing that Goodyear had not yet mastered the process, but Hancock, realising that the process must involve sulphur, as he had suspected, set feverishly to work in his own home labora-tory in Marlborough Cottage. In the meantime he used a useful wrinkle in English law that allowed him to take out a 'prelim-inary patent' on the idea, even though he couldn't yet fully describe the process. If he could fill in the details within six months, the patent would be ratified and enrolled. It was only eight weeks after this preliminary enrolment that Goodyear received his US patent.

Hancock claimed that over the winter of 1842/3 he mastered the process of treating rubber with sulphur to 'cure' it, or, in his words, 'bring about the change'. His patent was enrolled on 21 May 1844. As a result he should go down in history with the credit for inventing the process that his friend and colleague William Brockendon would christen 'vulcanisation', after the Roman god of fire.

The story, according to Stephen Moulton, who challenged the patent, is somewhat different. He claimed that Hancock, on receiving Goodyear's samples, immediately had his factory staff set to work analysing the material whilst himself taking out a preliminary patent even though he didn't yet understand the process. In rebuttal, Hancock argued that he had already been experimenting with sulphur for years, offering in support a signed affidavit from Brockendon, claiming that he had no knowledge of Hancock analysing Goodyear's samples.

Moulton countered with the testimony of a Hancock employee called Cooper who said he had indeed been set to work analysing Goodyear's rubber. Hancock then produced statements from a number of other distinguished chemists, asserting that it would be impossible, merely from analysing a sample, to deduce the process in the first place. Alexander Parkes, another rubber chemist, added fuel to the fire by saying that both Hancock and Brockendon had admitted to him that they *had* analysed Goodyear's sample. By this point everyone was rather confused, except Charles Macintosh, who had had the good sense to die whilst the storm was still brewing.

Despite this ungentlemanly spat, and the subsequent court case, which Goodyear attended, Hancock's patent stood and his business thrived. In his remaining years he described thousands of new objects and materials that could be made from his vulcanised rubber. Indeed, he lists nearly every modern use of rubber, from artificial sponges to 'ebonite' – a hard form of rubber that resists chemical action.

Yet despite his being undoubtedly one of the greatest pioneers in rubber use, as well as the first person to fully understand and control the process of vulcanisation, history has perhaps had the last say on apportioning credit. It is his partner Macintosh's name that is forever associated with waterproofs, and his American competitor, Goodyear, whose name would be read on the walls of millions of car tyres. Hancock's pickle meanwhile has remained resolutely the secret he always wanted it to be.

ↀ

Taking science out of the lab and into
the community doesn't always turn it into a
profitable business, however. Sometimes it
just makes people think you're odd.

ↀ

Snowflake Bentley

Nobody had really realised just how beautiful snowflakes were
until Wilson A. Bentley borrowed his mother's old microscope
in 1880.

Bentley was a farmer's son in Jericho in northern Vermont
so he was used to snow. In fact, the USA has the highest recorded
annual snowfall of anywhere on earth – including Antarctica –
a record held by Mount Baker in Washington state where, in
the winter of 1998/9, 28 metres of snow fell.

Just over a hundred years earlier, Bentley, a practical farm
boy, was the first person to realise that there was a benefit to
the freezing conditions that prevailed in his Jericho farmhouse
in those days. Indeed, it was so cold indoors that he could catch
snowflakes and look at them under the microscope in the parlour
before they melted, but melt they eventually did. As he later
wrote: 'Under the microscope, I found that snowflakes were
miracles of beauty; and it seemed a shame that this beauty should
not be seen and appreciated by others. Every crystal was a
masterpiece of design and no one design was ever repeated.
When a snowflake melted, that design was forever lost. Just that
much beauty was gone, without leaving any record behind.'

Bentley decided to preserve his snowflakes for ever – as photographs. Aided by $100 from his father (who thought he was mad),
he bought a camera to attach to the microscope and with this

primitive set-up, in 1885, he took the first photomicrographs of snowflakes, which proved the six-fold symmetry of ice crystals.

Sadly for Bentley, who spent the rest of his life photographing snowflakes, the academic establishment thought he was a mad farmer, while the people of Jericho thought he was a mad scientist, so no one took him very seriously. When he arranged to show the people of his home town his photographs – then the finest photomicrographs in existence – only six people turned up. Despite the fact that Vermontians were accustomed to being up to their ears in the stuff, it seems nobody was interested in snow.

During his lifetime, Bentley took 5,381 photographs of snowflakes (as well as making a definitive catalogue of 'the smiles of pretty girls' during the summer, which sounds like a lot more fun). Only in the very last years of the nineteenth century did his snowflake work receive any publicity, thanks to articles in *National Geographic* and *Scientific American*. These led to the only thing he is famous for today – the notion that every snowflake is unique, being, in his words, the individual work of the Creator.

More recently this idea has been queried, not least by Nancy Knight of the National Center for Atmospheric Research in the US, who discovered two snow crystals that, to all intents and purposes, had the same shape. However, the chances of finding two identical snowflakes 'in the wild' remains vanishingly small. It also perhaps misses the point. As the brilliantly analytical but also poetic Bentley put it: 'The snow crystals . . . come to us not only to reveal the wondrous beauty of the minute in Nature, but to teach us that all earthly beauty is transient and must soon fade away. But though the beauty of the snow is evanescent, like the beauties of the autumn, as of the evening sky, it fades but to come again.'

After a lifetime out in the cold chasing snowflakes, Wilson Bentley finally succumbed to pneumonia on 23 December 1931.

❧

In the nineteenth century few things
were considered more odd than a female
scientist and yet, in one of the most male-
dominated areas of a male-dominated discipline,
one woman proved that it really is only
talent that counts.

❧

Emily's bridge

There are few famous female engineers of the nineteenth century
and some would have it that this is because it is, by definition,
a male job. The story of Emily Warren Roebling suggests, very
firmly, otherwise.

The Roebling family were both blessed and cursed by bridges.
John Augustus Roebling had left a restive Prussia in 1831 for
what he hoped was the brave new world of America, only to
find it caught in the grip of a depression. For six years he made
a poor living as a farmer, before the brightening economic situation and the opening up of the still rather wild West brought
him back to his senses and to his first love: bridge-building.

In a country with ever expanding horizons, he proved a great
success, his crowning glory coming with the commission to build
the first bridge across the East river in New York to Long Island,
which would one day become known as the Brooklyn Bridge. It
was whilst surveying locations for the bridge in 1869 that he got
his foot caught on the edge of the dock, where it was crushed
by an incoming ferry. Following the amputation of his broken
toes, he refused further medical treatment and tetanus set in.
Just over three weeks later he was dead.

Fortunately for the Roebling business, and for Brooklyn, John's son Washington was waiting in the wings. Washington had been his father's deputy engineer and, in the years of political horse-trading whilst his father garnered support for the bridge, he and his young wife had been dispatched to Europe to learn the latest techniques in bridge-building. He would now put these into effect as he filled his father's somewhat mangled shoes.

It was three years later, with the deep pilings for the bridge supports well under way, that tragedy struck again. The pilings were being built using caissons – watertight structures driven into the river bed that could be pumped clear of water and in which the builders could then work. To keep the water out of the caissons, the whole interior was pressurised. What was very poorly understood at the time was that working in pressurised air forces excess nitrogen to dissolve in the bloodstream of those working at depth. If the pressure is released too quickly, the nitrogen simply bubbles out of the blood with potentially fatal consequences. Divers know this as 'the bends'. This is exactly what happened to Washington Roebling as he left the caisson after a twelve-hour stint on site. The result was excruciating agony, followed by permanent paralysis from the waist down.

Now paralysed and, on bad days, deaf and mute, Roebling could obviously no longer maintain his position as chief engin-eer of this flagship project, or so many thought. However, there was, once again, another Roebling waiting in the wings.

Emily Warren Roebling had met her husband Washington during the Civil War when he was serving in the Fifth Army Corps, which happened to be commanded by her brother. Less than a year later they were married and shortly afterwards they began the extended tour of Europe that her husband's father hoped would prepare his son for the task of building the Brooklyn Bridge. Fortunately, Emily had proved every bit as interested and adept as her husband in bridge-building. When he became incap-acitated, she announced that she would assume control of the project.

Of course in the early 1870s there was no chance that the all-male New York city fathers would allow a woman to officially take over as chief engineer, so Emily offered to act as the go-between for her husband. She alone would be allowed to see him as he inspected progress from his sickbed through binoculars, and she alone would pass on his instructions to the workforce. Washington would remain in charge but she would be the public face of the project for the next ten years of construction.

In truth, Emily, who was then just twenty-nine, rapidly proved far more than just a go-between. She studied mathematics and engineering, as well as learning the skills to deal with contractors (who often delivered substandard materials) and a workforce still sometimes killed by 'the bends'. By 1882 many working on the bridge had come to regard Emily as the chief engineer, directly asking her advice on progress rather than giving her messages for her husband.

Indeed, the role of Washington had declined to the point where a vindictive mayor of Brooklyn had petitioned that he be removed from his post. Emily, as much a politician as an engineer, and a better one than the mayor, requested permission to speak before the American Society of Engineers. It was the first time a woman had ever addressed that august body. Her eloquence quickly persuaded them to throw their weight behind her husband. He would stay on as chief engineer at least in name until the finish and she would continue as before.

The New York and Brooklyn Bridge, then the longest suspension bridge in the world, finally opened in May 1883 and Emily was the first person to 'officially' walk over it, as befitted the person with most right to claim it as her own. Washington Roebling was too ill to attend but the US president, having ceremoniously crossed the bridge himself, went to his home to shake his hand.

The politician, industrialist and later mayor of New York,

Abram Stevens Hewitt, made an opening address in which, in recognition of Emily, he called the bridge 'an everlasting monument to the sacrificing devotion of a woman and of her capacity for that higher education from which she had been too long disbarred'.

Emily further proved herself deserving of that higher education when she took a law degree at New York University in 1899. In her biography of her husband, who would eventually outlive her by twenty-six years, she, with typical modesty, thanked everyone who had helped with the bridge: 'It could never have been accomplished but for the unselfish devotion of his assistant engineers. Each man had a certain department to be in charge of and they worked with all their energies to have the work properly done according to Col. Roebling's plans and wishes.'

The only name she left out was her own, the true force behind the Brooklyn Bridge.

✺

Science is not always about working from first principles to deduce something. In the more practical fields it can just as easily be about realising that something we take for granted might have a different use. Even something that we find annoying.

✺

Velcro

George de Mestral was certainly annoyed. He had been walking his Irish pointer in the Jura mountains of his native Switzerland in 1941 and had returned home to find both his trousers and his dog's fur thick with sticky burdock burrs. Having spent hours picking the awkward seeds off both, he started to think about what made them hold on so tenaciously.

Fortunately de Mestral was an electrical engineer with a microscope to hand. He decided to investigate and what he saw intrigued him. The burrs were not 'sticky' but were covered in tiny hooks. These became tangled in the clothes (or fur) of passers-by to be carried off to pastures new where they might germinate, well away from their parent plant.

To de Mestral this seemed promising. What if he could synthetically create a material covered in tiny hooks and another covered in tiny loops? When put together, they'd form a strong bond but one that could still be pulled apart and repositioned. It could be a whole new way of fastening fabrics.

Of course nothing was quite that simple. Mimicking the masterpiece of a burdock burr, whose design has been honed through millions of years of evolution, was no small feat. In Lyons he persuaded a weaver to make a prototype but this cotton version soon wore out. He then settled on the new synthetic wonder fibre, nylon, which could be formed into tiny hooks using infra-red light. Ten more years passed whilst the techniques were perfected for manufacturing the material en masse.

His idea was finally submitted to the patent office in 1951. The name he chose was a combination of two French words, *velour* (velvet) and *crochet* (hook) – or velcro. The following year, with a $150,000 bank loan, he went into business, sure that the world's clothes manufacturers would beat a path to his door in their search for the material that he envisaged replacing laces, zippers and buttons. So it came as quite a surprise when they didn't.

Whilst velcro did exactly what he intended, it looked like a cheap plastic offcut – not something fashion-conscious clothes designers wanted on their clothes. Velcro might have been stillborn, were it not for a group with less of an interest in fashion and more of a need for practicality. With the space race under way, spacesuit designers were desperate to find efficient ways of fastening bulky spacesuits. Some of the first catwalks on which velcro appeared were gantries leading to rockets.

Where the space race led, other specialist clothing manufacturers followed. Soon the naturally corrosion-resistant velcro was to be seen on wetsuits, then on skiing outfits, where, in both cases, practicality outweighed appearance. Now that velcro was gaining some acceptability, it appeared next on children's clothes where it proved easier than buttons for little fingers to use. From one burdock burr at its outset, De Mestral's company had finally come of age and would end up producing over 55,000 kilometres of velcro a year.

∽

If much practical science can be said to
be about finding a practical use for a thing or
a phenomenon like the hooks on burdock burrs,
sometimes a good scientist turns that idea on its
head. Some things are worth making just for
the joy of it, regardless of their possible
use. We call these things toys.

∽

Slinky

It was December 1945 when Richard James walked into Gimbel's department store in Philadelphia, Pennsylvania, armed only with a wooden board and 400 small, paper-wrapped packages. In the toy department he was shown to his demonstration stand where he set his board on a slope, opened one of the packets his wife had so carefully wrapped the night before and tentatively began his demonstration. Outside, and unknown to Richard, his wife Betty and a friend were preparing to become his first customers, in the hope that an initial sale or two might encourage the others. They just hoped they weren't his only customers as, dollar bills in hand, they plunged into the throng.

The idea that Richard James, a naval engineer, was hoping to sell that day had come to him during the war, in 1943, when he had been working in Philadelphia's Cramp shipyard. He had been tasked with devising damping equipment to mount sensitive horsepower meters in the engine-rooms of battleships and was experimenting with arrangements of torsion springs. During one of these experiments he had casually knocked one of these springs off the table and noted something odd. Instead of just falling down in a heap, the spring rolled end on end, almost walking off the table on to the floor.

James was something of an inventor. Indeed, his was probably the only home in Philadelphia with ice-cold Coke on tap, courtesy of the compressor he had installed to pump the drink from the cellar straight into the fridge. As a result, his wife was not surprised when he came home saying he thought he might have invented a wonderful new toy. Suspicious, yes, but not surprised. Undeterred, James set to work looking for a steel with the correct properties that it could be coiled to the right tension to make a 'walking spring'. When he showed the prototype to his neighbour's children, even Betty was persuaded by their enthusiasm. Husband and wife decided to go into business.

With a $500 loan they set up the grandly named James Industries, spending most of the money having 400 springs made at a local machine shop. The rest went on single-colour printed sheets of instructions, which Betty would wrap around the spring to form its only packaging. With the springs wrapped and ready to go, all they needed was a name for their toy. After scouring the dictionary for hours, Betty found a word meaning 'stealthy, sleek and sinuous', which seemed to fit the bill. The word was, as you've guessed by now, 'slinky'.

For Richard, his try-out of his Slinky in the toy department at Gimbel's was his moment of truth. Betty stood in the doorway, preparing to pretend to be an eager customer. However, as she approached the Slinky stand, she rapidly saw that a fake purchase would be wholly unnecessary. The novelty was a surprising star hit and Richard was surrounded by real dollar-wielding customers. In his ninety-minute demonstration, he sold all 400 Slinkys and one of the iconic toys of the twentieth century was born.

The following year the Slinky was the most talked-about item at the US toy trade fair and the Jameses opened their own shop in Philadelphia. Betty set to work upgrading their packaging to a simple box while Richard used his engineering know-how to devise a machine that could coil the 80 feet of wire in each Slinky into the requisite ninety-eight coils in just under eleven seconds. By 1950 the toy was so successful that he'd had to build another five machines, all of which are still in operation today.

But it was not to be all fairytale endings for the Jameses. In 1960, Richard James suddenly decided to leave his business, his wife and his six children, to join what Betty called a 'religious cult' in Bolivia. Betty – down but not out – took over the business and paid off the large debts that had arisen from her husband's lavish donations to his new Bolivian friends. Moving the toy business back to her appropriately named home town of Holidaysburg, she not only saw off striking steel workers, but introduced new innovations such as the goggle-eyed Slinky glasses, the Slinky dog (made yet more famous by the *Toy Story* movies) and the plastic Slinky. In 1998, aged eighty, she finally agreed to sell the company so she could spend more time with her family.

The Jameses' best-selling toy remains to this day the Slinky itself, whose only alterations over the past half-century have been the introduction of crimped ends (for safety reasons) and the transition from Swedish blue steel to a cheaper American steel. There is a Slinky in the Smithsonian, a Slinky has been in space, and the toy has even been honoured with its own US Postal Service stamp. Most importantly of all, over 300 million of these simple engineering components have been sold to children across the world, contributing to many hundreds of thousands of very happy Christmases for everyone except the grown-up given the job of untangling the thing.

The Second World War is an unlikely place to go hunting for science-based toys but Slinkys are not alone. In a time when science is driven by a deadly imperative, lots of things turn up that don't work out as useful as was hoped. But a good scientist never throws things away.

Oops, there goes another rubber-tree plant

Many unexpected discoveries emerge from the maelstrom of war and by no means are all of them military. In fact, one of the more innocuous and popular of these owes its existence, oddly enough, to Japanese military expansion through the Far East in the 1940s.

One of the immediate effects of Japanese forces taking control of large areas of South-East Asia was the threat this posed to the supply of rubber in the West. From electrical insulation to waterproof coats to lorry tyres and boot soles, rubber was an essential ingredient in the prosecution of the war. With Japan now able to choke off the Allies' supply of the raw material latex, an alternative became essential.

In the USA the job of finding this replacement was given to the War Production Board, which put out a request to the

American chemical industry for the creation of a synthetic rubber. This request eventually landed on the laboratory bench of James Wright, a Scottish engineer working for the General Electric Company at their New Haven research facility in Connecticut. He began to experiment with silicone oil, which he thought structurally similar enough to be of interest. However, when he added boric acid, a plasticiser, to the oil, he was disappointed. Instead of forming a solid rubbery lump, the oil transformed into a soft, gooey material – with some interesting properties. When dropped, it bounced, just like rubber, but if left in a ball it would slowly flow to form a pool. When submitted to a sudden shock, it shattered.

Interesting as this was, the material was clearly not a rubber substitute. Who wants a tyre that shatters when you hit a pothole and oozes down the drain when you come to a stop? Unable to find anything to do with the substance except christen it 'bouncy putty', researchers moved on. It was 1945 before Wright made another attempt at finding an application for his invention by sending out samples to engineers.

For four years the finest engineering minds in the world failed to come up with anything that could be done with the putty. It was noted that as well as bouncing, shattering and flowing, it could lift newsprint, clean lint from clothes and make a reasonable adhesive, but nothing really stood out.

It was only in 1949 that a sample reached a more unexpected researcher. Ruth Fallgatter, who was looking for things to put in the catalogue for her toyshop, asked a friend and marketing consultant, Peter Hodgson, whether this substance might make a good toy. Agreeing that, whilst the putty had no obvious single use, its strange properties made it an ideal novelty, they began packaging small pieces of the stuff.

Although the putty sold well, Peter Hodgson thought there might be more in it and pursued the idea on his own. Despite being heavily in debt, he borrowed further and in February 1950 took a batch of one-ounce lumps to the International Toy Fair in New York. As the next big holiday after the fair would be Easter, he packaged the putty in a plastic egg. He also decided he needed a new name for the material and, after considering fifteen possibilities, settled on Silly Putty.

Silly Putty proved no great hit at the fair but Hodgson persevered. When *The New Yorker* magazine ran an item on the putty, which was then marketed as a novelty for adults, sales suddenly took off and over three days 250,000 orders flooded in. With a brief interruption during the Korean War, when the supply of silicone oil was restricted by the US government, Silly Putty went from strength to strength, being rebranded as a children's toy and even making it into space on *Apollo 8* as a means of securing tools in weightless conditions. By the late 1980s over 2 million eggs were being produced each year. The material with no use had found its natural home.

∽

And as we're in playful mood, something for the grown-ups.

∽

Pie in the sky

The best new ideas sometimes come out of left field and, in the case of the frisbee, this was literally the case.

Its story begins, unpromisingly enough, in 1871 in Bridgeport, Connecticut, where William Russell Frisbie had set up a bakery, close by Yale University. There he hoped to do a roaring trade, selling ready-made pies to hungry undergraduates whose culinary skills began and ended with boiling eggs. Pies and cakes were tricky to transport, so Frisbie packaged his in cheap metal tins with the words 'Frisbie's Pies', not unreasonably, embossed on the base. For the gentlemen scholars of Yale, this provided another incentive to buy the pies once they discovered that the discarded tins had an aerofoil shape that allowed them to fly long distances if thrown with a flick of the wrist.

During the early years of the following century, the idea of throwing around pie tins or metal lids of any variety met with moderate success but could hardly be called a craze. It was not until 1937 that this changed when Walter Frederick Morrison was approached on a Californian beach by a man who wanted to buy his popcorn lid. According to Morrison, he and his girl-friend Lu had been throwing the discarded lid to each other when an interested bystander, liking the game, offered to buy it from them for twenty-five cents. Morrison realised that if he could sell a five-cent lid for twenty-five cents, he might have the makings of a business. After some market research revealed that metal pie tins were more robust and flew better, the couple set up in business selling 'Flyin' Cake Pans'.

Before it could really get going, Morrison found himself flying for real, in a P47 Thunderbolt, as a pilot in the Second World War. It was during a spell as a prisoner of war that he got a chance to think more about his flying pie tins. After repatria-tion he first sketched the 'Whirlo-Way', a bespoke plastic flying disc. In 1948, having craftily changed the name to 'Flyin' Saucer' to cash in on interest surrounding the previous year's Roswell UFO incident, he took the disc to market.

Further refinements followed – Morrison had learnt a lot about aerodynamics from flying in the war – and in 1955 he released the 'Pluto Platter', an improved disc that piqued the interest of the equally eccentrically named Wham-O toy corporation. Two years later he sold the patent to them but success remained somewhat elusive.

Indeed, it was only some time later that the co-founder of Wham-O, Richard Knerr, discovered part of the problem, whilst trying to promote the flying disc on college campuses. Here he found that students were still happily throwing pie tins at each other, as they had been for decades. In fact, they even had a name for the sport – frisbie – after the eponymous pie maker. Once it had taken on the nickname and its spelling had judiciously been changed to frisbee, the flying disc finally took off.

7

Accidents, Errors and Unintended Consequences

(In which things go a bit wrong but then generally end up all right or even better. With a few exceptions.)

The great tragedy of Science – the slaying of a beautiful hypothesis by an ugly fact.

T.H. Huxley, 'Biogenesis and Abiogenesis', in *Collected Essays* (1893–4)

~ঌ~

Science, like stock trading, requires a lot
of luck, however good you are at it, and even
the best scientists can make mistakes, leading to
the most surprising of consequences. This
is how conspiracy theories are born . . .

~ঌ~

The moons of Mars

In 1726 the author Jonathan Swift wrote an extraordinary para-
graph in Part Three of his great work, *Travels into Several
Remote Nations of the World, in Four Parts. By Lemuel Gulliver,
First a Surgeon, and then a Captain of several Ships*, or *Gulliver's
Travels*, as it is more succinctly known. In talking about the
inhabitants of the flying island of Laputa, he states that 'They
have made a Catalogue of ten Thousand fixed Stars, whereas
the largest of ours do not contain above one third Part of that
Number. They have likewise discovered two lesser Stars, or
Satellites, which revolve about Mars.'

At the time this came as something of a surprise to the
gentlemen of the Royal Society, whom Swift was satirising in
the Laputians, as Mars had no known moons. Yet this was fiction
after all. What came as significantly more of a surprise, 151
years later, was the discovery by Asaph Hall of the US Naval
Observatory that Mars did indeed have two moons, similar to
the ones Swift describes. The question was – how could he have
known?

The answer to this strange conundrum, which has spawned
numerous conspiracy theories over the years, including suggestions
that Swift was himself a Martian, actually has to do with a letter
sent in 1610 to the great German astronomer Johannes Kepler in

Augsburg. It read: 'Smaismrmilmepoetaleumibunenugttauiras.'

Kepler was used to receiving this sort of letter and was delighted that Galileo Galilei (see page 297) had decided to confide in him, if somewhat cryptically. The word was, of course, a code – in fact, an anagram. Sending such messages allowed scientists, in an era before copyrights and patents, to establish who had first made a particular discovery. The coded announcement of a find would be sent to other eminent scientists while the discoverer undertook further work, confirming it. Then, when he was happy that he was right, the announcement would be made official and everyone could check that that was in fact what the anagram had said.

Kepler, however, was not good at waiting and decided he would pre-empt Galileo by unpicking the anagram himself, although he was not much good at anagrams either. After much frustration he finally came out with the revelatory message: 'Salue umbistineum geminatum Martia proles', which can be roughly translated as: 'Hail, twin companionship, offspring of Mars'.

In reality, the anagram was one letter out but what else could it mean? After all, Galileo had previous form for discovering the moons of other planets – he'd been the first to raise a primitive telescope to Jupiter and see its four largest moons. The result also chimed with Kepler's own mathematical work, which, following the detection of Jupiter, had suggested that Mars might have two moons, if too small to be seen with the telescopes of the day. Kepler told his boss, the Holy Roman Emperor Rudolf II, that Galileo had found there to be two new moons around Mars – just as he had predicted.

Except he hadn't. In a flurry of excitement, the news passed round the courts of Europe, until the Tuscan ambassador to the Holy Roman Empire, Giuliano de' Medici, who had often carried letters between Galileo and Kepler, told Galileo that the emperor himself wished confirmation of the find and could he please provide it. Galileo, not liking to disappoint emperors, provided the solution: 'Altissimum Planetam Tergeminum Obseravi'.

This was rather different from Kepler's version and can be translated as: 'I have observed the highest [most distant] planet [Saturn] to be of triple form.' In short, nothing to do with Mars at all.

Galileo had been pointing his telescope at Saturn, not Mars, but, with such a primitive instrument, he was unable to resolve the ring system around it. What he saw in his blurry eyepiece was what appeared to be a central planet with two 'ears' attached to it – hence the announcement about Saturn's 'triple form'.

Kepler was left blushing but his suggestion that Mars 'should' have moons didn't go away. He knew the earth had one moon, and Jupiter had four, so, working on a simple geometrical progression, he reasoned that Mars, which lies in between those two planets, must have two.

Thus the idea that Mars might have moons – allied perhaps to a memory of the humbling of the great Kepler – passed down a century to the age of Swift, who, in gently satirising the gentlemen of the Royal Society, resurrected the tale in the magical flying land of Laputa, in the process pre-empting the real discovery of Mars' moons by a century and a half, but for all the wrong reasons.

❧

Sometimes accidental discoveries prove
surprisingly useful. They might turn up in
the form of an experiment gone wrong, in the
observation of an unusual phenomenon, or in
something as everyday and unremarkable
as a fly buzzing into a room.

❧

Where am I?

René Descartes did most of his best work in bed. As a child
he'd developed the habit of lying in until lunchtime, not because
he was lazy but because of his famously weak constitution. Even
at school (the Jesuit college of La Flèche), the masters allowed
him a lie-in during the morning. In bed Descartes would think;
indeed, it's probably thanks to those late mornings that he
became one of the greatest thinkers of his age. And one of the
concepts he invented when tucked up in bed would become a
cornerstone of modern mathematics – and the modern world.

The story of how Descartes came to this revelation may or
may not be true – there is a suspicious correlation between mathematical discoveries and amazing anecdotes – but, if nothing
else, it provides a good explanation for what he was thinking.

The forty-one-year-old Descartes was, as usual, in bed, looking
up at the ceiling, when he noticed a fly crawling across it. An ordinary man might have reached for a newspaper to swat the creature
but Descartes was different. He began to wonder: how do I know
where that fly is? Again, a simpler person might have replied, 'It's
on the ceiling,' but Descartes wanted to know exactly where it was
and the answer he came up with was as simple as it was elegant.

He realised that the position of the fly could be determined by measuring the distance to it horizontally along one wall and then the corresponding distance up the perpendicular wall. Effectively the ceiling was a huge graph with two axes joined at the corner. By defining the fly's distance along each, he could say where the fly was and describe where it was going. He had invented what we now call Cartesian co-ordinates (Descartes published using the Latin version of his name, Cartesius), the origin of every X and Y on every graph and in every equation.

In truth, he was not the first person to have this idea. Pierre de Fermat, made famous by his 'Last Theorem', had already worked out a co-ordinate system for three dimensions, but he hadn't got round to publishing it. The tenth-century Persian polymath Al-Biruni had got there centuries before him, although his work was unknown in the West. So it was Descartes that got the glory for developing the co-ordinate system that would lead to Newton's and Leibniz's (see page 75) calculus, as well as all those equations, integrations and differentiations that have baffled schoolchildren for centuries since. All thanks to a boy who never even showed up to his morning lessons as he was still in bed.

✌

Good science is often about things going wrong. This leads to a theory of what is causing the trouble, which can then be tested. But it is not always the scientists themselves who make the breakthrough. Sometimes they just need to be there to see it happen.

✌

Beriberi

In the late nineteenth century news reached Europe that the people of the Dutch East Indies were being struck down by a terrible epidemic. The early symptoms were tiredness, irritability and pains in the abdomen, which could develop into a burning sensation in the extremities, followed by numbness. Heart attacks often followed closely on the heels of these symptoms and autopsies showed the heart muscle to have been severely wasted. This was not a new disease but the well-known beriberi, which had been afflicting populations, particularly sailors, for centuries. The question was: why had it sprung up just then and in that particular place with such severity?

The Dutch authorities decided, in 1886, to send out a commission to investigate. Clemens Winkler and Cornelis Pekelharing were assigned the job and before leaving they took the opportunity to visit the most famous biological laboratories of the day. In the lab of Robert Koch in Berlin, they met fellow Dutchman Christiaan Eijkman. Eijkman seemed like an ideal assistant to take along. He had worked in the East Indies before contracting malaria and being sent home. More importantly, he had since then worked with Koch, the pioneer of germ theory, which had identified the cause of many diseases as being tiny micro-organisms (see page 269). Clearly the beriberi epidemic must be caused by one of these, making Eijkman perfectly placed to help identify it.

The commission arrived in Java to find the situation to be critical. In the larger towns nearly half of all newborn babies were dying from the disease and even healthy adults were succumbing to its apparently relentless spread. Work immediately began on identifying the pathogen responsible and within a year a candidate had supposedly been isolated. At this point Winkler and Pekelharing were rather precipitously recalled, leaving Eijkman to tie up what were considered to be no more than the 'loose ends'.

But Eijkman wasn't happy. He had been trying to infect rabbits and monkeys with the bacterium his colleagues had found but the animals stubbornly refused to get sick. Reasoning that perhaps the disease had a long incubation period, he experimented on an animal with a faster rate of development – chickens. The chickens worked a treat and in just a month they had all developed beriberi. In fact, if anything, the experiment had worked too well: not only did the chickens he had injected with the bacterium have beriberi – so did those he hadn't. He could only assume that the sick animals had somehow passed it on to the healthy ones.

In an attempt to contain the spread, he brought in fresh chickens and kept them quarantined away from the others, but they too developed the disease. Eventually concluding that the whole laboratory must be infested, he began keeping chickens at a different site – but these too got sick.

Then, quite suddenly, something extraordinary happened. All the birds suddenly recovered. Eijkman knew that if he could uncover what it was that had changed, he might discover the cure. He found his answer in the kitchen. The only element that had changed at the very time that the chickens recovered was the cook. Food for the birds was provided by the military hospital to which his laboratory was attached and the previous cook had sent Eijkman the leftover cooked rice to feed to them each day. The new cook, however, didn't want to waste rice meant for human consumption on chickens, so he sent over raw, 'unpolished' rice, which had not had the 'silver skin' (pericarpium) removed from each seed. When the birds started eating this, they all miraculously got better.

Eijkman had his 'smoking gun' but he still didn't understand why the rice was curing his chickens. In fact, he came to the wrong conclusion. Noting that the cooked rice made the birds ill, he started a series of controlled tests, feeding chickens cooked and uncooked, polished and unpolished rice. He concluded that there must be something in cooked rice that helped an unknown micro-organism to breed and produce poison in the chickens' intestines. He also noted that the 'silver skins', when fed to ill birds, made them well again, which led him to deduce that they contained the magical antidote, or 'anti-beriberi factor' as he called it.

If Eijkman's reasoning was not right, his observations were spot on. Nine more years of work on animals convinced him that it was the rice husks that saved lives and in 1895 he managed to persuade a doctor to carry out tests on humans in a local prison (see page 224). Again the results were astounding. Those prisoners who ate unpolished rice remained healthy whereas those who ate the more fashionable polished rice got ill.

What Eijkman had stumbled upon, although he didn't know it, was not a micro-organism, but a vitamin. The silver skins contained not an anti-beriberi factor, but the vitamin B_I (thiamine). Since the 1870s the Dutch had been importing to their colonies steam-driven rice-milling and polishing machines, which produced the clean, white rice that at the time was preferred. This vogue soon spread – critically, to a population for whom rice wasn't an occasional dish but their staple food. With its silver skin removed the rice had no B_I and as a result beriberi, caused by a lack of this vitamin, swept through the population.

Although Eijkman was not aware of this, his successor in Batavia, Gerrit Grijns, made that intellectual leap. In 1912 the British biochemist Frederick Hopkins finally isolated the magical substance B_I, just a year after Casimir Funk had coined the word 'vitamin'. Eijkman and Hopkins were jointly awarded the Nobel prize for their work in 1929.

ৎ৩

Sometimes it is an interest – or an interesting
accident – in one field that leads a scientist
to a discovery in another.

ৎ৩

The touch of silk

The story of artificial silk should probably begin with Robert
Hooke (see page 19), who noted in 1664:

> I have often thought, that probably there might be a way
> found out, to make an artificial glutinous composition,
> much resembling, if not full as good, nay better, than that
> Excrement, or whatever other substance it be out of which,
> the Silk-worm wire-draws his clew. If such a composition
> were found, it were certainly an easie matter to find very
> quick ways of drawing it out into small wires for use. I
> need not mention the use of such an Invention, nor the
> benefit that is likely to accrue to the finder, they being suffi-
> ciently obvious. This hint therefore, may, I hope, give some
> Ingenious inquisitive Person an occasion of making some
> trials, which if successfull, I have my aim, and I suppose
> he will have no occasion to be displeas'd.

It proved to be a good 'hint' but it would be nearly 200 years
before anyone would take it up. Louis-Marie Hilaire Bernigaud
de Chardonnet had got to know something of silkworms when
working with the great Louis Pasteur (see page 109).

In 1865, at a time when Chardonnet was one of his assistants, Pasteur had been asked by the French silk industry to advise
on a potentially terminal problem. French silkworms were being

decimated by two diseases, flacherie and pébrine, for which neither the cause nor the cure was known. Pasteur and his assistants eventually concluded that flacherie was caused by the larvae eating infected mulberry leaves, and pébrine by a tiny parasite. The solution, they advised, was to destroy the entire infected stock of both mulberry and silkworms, and start again. It was a bitter pill but one that the French silk industry swallowed, which saved it.

Whilst studying silkworms, Chardonnet had plenty of time to wonder at the strange thread they spun and how they did it, as well as pondering how the effect might be artificially replicated. Only some years later did a potential silk substitute accidentally come his way.

Chardonnet was a man of wealth, who, not having to work, dedicated his life to the sciences and one of his particular interests was photography. In the early days of cameras, a photographer had to prepare his own plates and, as Chardonnet used the wet-plate collodion (see page 241) process, this was laborious. First, a glass plate had to be scrupulously cleaned before collodion – a highly flammable, sticky solution of nitrocellulose (guncotton) – was poured over it. This plate was taken to a dark room and immersed in silver nitrate solution. The resulting photographic plate would be loaded into a plate holder and exposed in a camera before the image was developed and fixed.

It was during the first part of this process that Chardonnet knocked over and broke his jar of collodion. Having finished preparing his plates, he returned to the partly dried mess and began trying to clear it up. When he dabbed the spill with a cloth, he noticed that the collodion now formed into extremely fine silk-like strands. Could this be the answer to making artificial silk?

The process of turning a photographic plate into a silk dress would not prove an easy one. For six years he worked in private, developing both the nitrocellulose solution, which he derived from mulberry leaves, and a spinneret to extrude the gluey substance. In 1884 he applied for, and was granted, a French patent.

Finally, in 1889, Chardonnet unveiled his artificial silk to the world at the Paris Exhibition. It proved an instant success. Although Chardonnet had not been strictly the first to create an artificial silk (that honour probably goes to George Audemars in 1855 and to J.W. Swan in 1879), his was a process that could be scaled up to industrial manufacture. Unlike Swan's silk, which was just for use in light-bulb filaments, Chardonnet's silk could be worn.

By 1891, artificial silk was in full production. If there was a drawback it was perhaps the fabric's alarming flammability, being derived from guncotton. This led its detractors in the real silk industry to refer to it as 'mother-in-law silk', as you'd want to give such a volatile fabric only to your mother-in-law. And then perhaps offer her a cigarette?

∽

Chance of course plays its part in every science but it is not just the chance accident or observation that can lead to revelation. Sometimes it's just a good, old-fashioned human misunderstanding.

∽

Riemann's third choice

Euclid's book *Stoichia* (*Elements*) is probably the most popular textbook of all time. The book was compiled around 300 BC by the Greek known as the 'father of geometry', using some of the work of earlier mathematicians, and its mathematical system is still taught to every maths student today. Since its first printing in Venice in 1482, at least a thousand editions have been published – more than any other book except the Bible.

So it is not surprising that the contents of the *Elements* are revered by many a mathematician (see page 25), sometimes to the point of being taken almost as gospel. This placed Georg Friedrich Bernhard Riemann in a difficult position as he prepared to give the most important lecture of his life in 1854.

Riemann had originally been intended for the priesthood but had managed to persuade his father that a career in mathematics would suit him better. At the University of Göttingen, where the great mathematician Carl Friedrich Gauss (see page 233) worked, he soon changed courses from theology and philology to mathematics.

Here he studied Euclid whose five 'postulates' lay at the heart of all geometry. The last of these, Postulate 5, states: 'If two lines are drawn which intersect a third in such a way that the sum of the inner angles on one side is less than two right angles, then the two lines inevitably must intersect each other on that side if extended far enough.' Put another way, given any straight line and a point that is not on it, there exists one and only one straight line that passes through that point and never intersects the first line, no matter how far they are extended. In other words, parallel lines never meet.

All five postulates were taken as unequivocally true – well, nearly – for, as Riemann and a few others knew, the last postulate could not be proven as a theorem. This inconvenient difficulty with geometry was normally put aside, and for now that is just what Riemann did.

Riemann – a brilliant, if chronically shy, student – returned to Göttingen after a spell in Berlin to settle into an academic career. The one hurdle that stood in his way, however, was his need to give a *Habilitationsvortrag* – a lecture to the staff of the faculty – which, if successful, would allow him to become a *Privatdozent*. These were lecturers who were allowed to teach in return for fees from their students, as the university didn't pay them a salary. Riemann was poor and, not having a staff job, needed the money, so he applied.

The format for the *Habilitationsvortrag* was both well established and bound up with tradition. The applicant would suggest to the head of the department three titles for possible lectures but would prepare only the first two. The head of department (in Riemann's case, Gauss) would choose which the applicant should give, always considerately choosing one of the first two. Riemann prepared two lectures on subjects he was very familiar with but submitted three titles, the last of which, as a casual throwaway, he entitled: 'On the Hypotheses which lie at the foundation of Geometry'.

Perhaps no one had told Gauss what the considerate convention was, because when he saw the provocative third title, he promptly chose that. In truth, Gauss had his own little geometric secret and was fascinated to learn what Riemann might have to say about the subject. In public, Gauss supported the five propositions – the foundations of geometry – as laid down by Euclid, but in private he had his doubts. Along with two other mathematicians, Janós Bolyai and Nikolai Lobachevsky, he had begun to realise that there were non-Euclidean geometries where Euclid's postulates, particularly the fifth, just might not hold true. This was almost a heresy in geometry and Gauss actually suppressed his results. But what would the brilliant Riemann do?

Initially, the brilliant Riemann panicked. On the day of the lecture he was totally unprepared, stumbling over his opening words. As he warmed to his task, however, he began to speak more freely, coming back to a subject he had often privately thought about – alternative geometries. In particular he pointed out that there were everyday examples where Euclid's rules clearly did not apply – on a sphere, for instance. Here lines of longitude all cross the Equator at 90 degrees to it and so are parallel, yet at the poles they meet. And a triangle, any triangle, drawn on a sphere has internal angles that add up to more than 90 degrees.

It was to be one of the great moments in the history of mathematics. In an hour Riemann outlined a world beyond Euclid, and not just one world but a universe of different but consistent geometries, stretching over an infinite number of dimensions. Riemann had said what Gauss would not, in doing so transforming geometry. Needless to say, he got the job.

∽

Something most scientists would agree
on (with the possible exception of Alexander
Fleming) is that good laboratory practice is
essential. Experiments must be done in a clearly
recorded and hence repeatable way. If not,
it can lead to disaster. Then again, it
can also lead to triumph.

∽

Unmarked bottles

Experimental scientists are a famously careful bunch – recording exactly what they do at each stage of an experiment and with what, so that their results are reproducible. Without this, science would be in a mess, but occasionally it is the very mess produced when this goes wrong that produces the breakthrough.

In 1948, Christopher Polge arrived at the National Institute for Medical Research in Mill Hill, London, fresh from a degree in agriculture. Here he and his new colleague Audrey Smith were put to work by the professor, Alan Parkes, on the tricky problem of fowl sperm. What fascinated Parkes was the possibility of freezing chicken sperm and using it for artificial insemination, but every time he froze samples, the cells died. His students' job was to find a way around this.

Polge and Smith set to work with great vigour, experimenting with a number of solutions (known now as cryoprotectants), in particular the fruit sugar fructose, which they thought might protect the sperm from the build-up of damaging ice crystals as they froze. After several months' work the situation looked hopeless and the work was put aside.

Six months later Polge, himself the son of a poultry farmer, moved to the farm site attached to the laboratories to be closer to his chickens, asking for the cryoprotectants that he and Smith had prepared earlier to be sent to him there. He tried the experiments again, adding his old supply of now mouldy fructose to fowl sperm and then freezing it to minus 79 degrees Centigrade. Astonishingly, when he thawed out this new sample, the sperm were still active, so active, in fact, that he tried inseminating chickens with it, leading to the birth of one chick.

It was only a small start but it was the first hint that the process was possible. He ran the experiment again. Having made up some fresh fructose solution, he froze the sperm, only to find that, on thawing, they were all dead – so what had changed? Polge soon realised that there must be something special about the old mouldy fructose solution. Draining the last of this precious fluid from the jar, he sent it to the analytical chemist D.F. Elliot. Elliot reported back that the solution contained no sugars at all, but a lot of glycerol, some water and a bit of protein.

That might not sound familiar to you or me, but Polge recognised that the substance described sounded uncannily like

Mayer's Albumen, a mixture of egg albumen and glycerol used to prepare microscope samples. He and Smith now tried producing samples using this standard laboratory chemical and, sure enough, the sperm survived the freezing. Further experiment showed that it was solely the glycerol in the fluid that provided protection and, thanks to this, the whole subject of cryobiology was born.

Polge would later note, 'Nobody will ever know exactly what happened,' but the truth of the matter was that lax experimental control and poor labelling were probably the two main forces behind the discovery. It would appear that the labels on the bottles of fructose, which had been stored in the original lab, had fallen off and had been reaffixed later. In the process one of the labels had ended up on a bottle of stale Mayer's Albumen. This had been delivered to Polge who, against all accepted procedures, had experimented with the mouldy liquid instead of making up a new batch. Had it not been for these two pieces of what today would be considered appalling laboratory technique, cryobiology might still be in its infancy.

∽

Not every accident leads to a new
invention and not every misunderstanding
leads to a new discovery. Sometimes it's
just best to be on the safe side.

∽

The Maud Committee

In the early years of the Second World War, a worrying possibility haunted both the corridors of power and the laboratories of physicists in Britain. In 1939, the exiled physicist Otto Frisch, then working in Birmingham, had, along with his aunt Lise Meitner (see page 56), been the first to demonstrate nuclear fission. It had become rapidly apparent to them that this technology might be put to use in a bomb of extraordinary power, which would still be compact enough to fit in the bomb-bay of an ordinary aircraft.

Frisch had made notes on how such a theoretical weapon might be constructed and, considering the danger presented by this knowledge – much of which was also available to the Germans, he sent these papers, together with those of his colleague Rudolph Peierls, to Sir Henry Tizard, one of the government's chief scientific advisors.

This Frisch–Peierls memorandum, as it became known, rapidly led to the creation of a committee to study proposals for nuclear weapons, to be chaired by Sir George Thompson, although neither Frisch nor Peierls, who were technically enemy aliens, could sit on it. A committee studying such a secret and potentially devastating subject needed a code name, the idea for which also came from Frisch. He had received a cryptic telegram from his aunt Lise Meitner who was then (May 1940) in neutral Sweden. She wrote: 'MET NIELS AND MARGHERITA RECENTLY. BOTH WELL BUT UNHAPPY ABOUT EVENTS. PLEASE INFORM COCKCROFT AND MAUD RAY KENT.'

The Niels referred to was, of course, the legendary Danish physicist and amateur footballer (see page 43) Niels Bohr, who was living in Denmark, which had just been invaded by Germany. Obviously, Niels, who came from a Jewish family, wanted to let his old friend John Cockcroft know that he and his wife Margherita were safe despite the invasion, but what did the rest of the message mean? Was Bohr possibly being forced to put his brilliant mind to work for the Nazi atomic programme? This was a pressing matter as the very idea was unthinkable.

In London, Cockcroft was shown the telegram and thought

that the 'ray' referred to might be some kind of physical ray. The intelligence services were quickly put to work on the text as it now seemed likely that Bohr might have been sending some vital coded information on nuclear technology. Did he perhaps have the key to creating a nuclear device and was he smuggling the secret out of occupied Denmark in code?

Cryptographers went to work on the words 'MAUD RAY KENT' and suggested that if the Y were substituted with an I, it became an anagram of 'RADIUM TAKEN'. Clearly this was indeed a nuclear code. Another expert suggested it read 'MAKE UR DAY NT', which might be a cryptic reference to possible uranium decay. Whatever the words meant, they were clearly important to the whole nuclear project. Thompson decided to call his committee the Maud Committee.

It was only three years later that the true meaning of the mysterious telegram – and hence the name of Britain's nuclear weapons committee – actually came to light. In 1943, Niels Bohr, aware he was about to be arrested by the German authorities, managed to escape to Sweden and from there made his way to London. In London he naturally enough asked whether Lise Meitner had passed on his message. Most specifically, had anyone told his children's old governess, Maud Ray, that the family were safe? She was, he told them, living in Kent.

ᔯ

As many a scientist who has found
themselves in court can tell you, there is
nothing more dangerous than an argument
where you know you are 100 per cent,
scientifically provably right. In so doing you
assume your opposing number to be equally
logical – which can be a very big mistake.

ᔯ

Flat earth

Alfred Russel Wallace was one of the leading lights of the
nineteenth-century evolutionary movement; indeed, it was his
independent work on natural selection that finally motivated
Darwin to publish his own theory. One of the great scientists
of the era, Wallace was keen to promote clear thinking and to
counter superstition, yet the greatest financial disaster of his life
would be his wager to prove what he considered the most self-
evident fact of all: that the earth was not flat.

Wallace was never rich, so the opportunity to make some
money was always welcome. Just such an opportunity apparently presented itself on 12 January 1870 in the journal *Scientific
Opinion*, where one John Hampden had placed an advertisement offering a wager of between £50 and £500 (£500 having
the buying power of around £35,000 today) to anyone who could
prove that the earth was not flat.

It seemed like easy money. The 'Flat Earthers' were an eccentric bunch endlessly chipping away at the edges of science with
their ludicrous claim. The ancient Greeks had known, and
proved, that the earth was a globe – any sailor in the port of
London could tell you as much – and yet they insisted that this

was not the case. With the encouragement of another academic giant of the day, the geologist Charles Lyell, Wallace set out to take Hampden's money.

Wallace, who happened to be a qualified surveyor, proposed to set up an experiment on a dead-straight, 6-mile length of canal known as the Old Bedford river, on the Bedford Level. Along that length he proposed to set up three poles, one at each end and one in the middle, all exactly the same distance above the water level. If the earth was flat, then the water would be flat too and so, when the poles were viewed through a telescope, they would all appear at the same height. Wallace knew, of course, that the earth was round and that therefore the surface of the water would be imperceptibly curved, making the middle pole appear higher than the other two.

With two witnesses (a Mr Coulcher for Wallace and a Mr Carpenter for Hampden), the experiment was set up. The result should have been a foregone conclusion but, as Wallace puts it in his autobiography, it 'cost me fifteen years of continued worry, litigation, and persecution, with the final loss of several hundred pounds'.

With the experiment in place, Hampden's witness, Mr Carpenter, was asked to look through the telescope, which clearly showed the middle pole to be higher, proving the surface of the water was curved. Mr Carpenter took a look and agreed but claimed that it proved nothing as the telescope was not level. A spirit level was therefore brought and the telescope levelled. Carpenter looked again and, according to Wallace, 'actually jumped for joy'. Rather surprisingly, he told Hampden that the three marks were in perfect alignment, which of course they weren't.

Wallace asked both witnesses to sketch what they saw in the telescope. They did so, both sketches clearly showing the middle mark to be higher. Carpenter, however, resolutely maintained, despite his own drawing, that the three were in perfect alignment. Hampden was then asked to look but refused to put his eye to the telescope, announcing instead that he'd won.

It must have been difficult for Wallace to know quite what to do in this situation but he eventually suggested that perhaps an independent referee should look at the sketches and decide. Finally they agreed that Mr J.H. Walsh, editor of *The Field*, would be a good choice. In the meantime the £500 was put into Walsh's safe keeping. In the issues for 18 and 26 March, Walsh published the experiment, the sketches and his decision, which, not surprisingly, was in favour of Wallace. He then wrote to Hampden, telling him he was handing over the stake to Wallace, but Hampden wrote back, demanding the return of his stake and refuting the claim.

Hampden clearly had some knowledge of some obscure legal precedent, for Walsh had made a mistake. According to the law at the time, if the loser claimed the stake back from the stake-holder (Mr Walsh) before he handed it over to the winner, the money had to be returned. This would eventually lead to Wallace's undoing.

Hampden (who, in truth, was a shade deranged) now began a sixteen-year hate campaign against Wallace and Walsh, publishing libellous pamphlets about the two, denouncing them as swindlers and cheats, and writing to their circle of friends and colleagues with similar claims. He then began writing to Mrs Wallace, threatening violence against her husband, which finally got him arrested. A week in prison did not stop the attacks, however, so Wallace sued for libel. Hampden, slippery as ever, did not contest the charge but by the time a fine was set he had handed over all his worldly goods to his son-in-law (a lawyer), so Wallace not only received nothing but had to pay all the costs of the court case.

Further trials followed. Hampden was eventually returned to gaol once more but on his release he had one further trick up his sleeve. He now brought a case against Wallace for the return of the £500.

As Walsh had been in error in not immediately handing over the money to Wallace, the court case went against him and Wallace was forced to pay back the £500. He was, however, still owed £687 by Hampden from previous libel trials and hoped to set this off against the claim. As Hampden had (fraudulently) had himself declared bankrupt, Wallace was left with his own, Walsh's and Hampden's costs, as well as paying up on the wager. In grateful thanks Hampden went straight back to publishing libellous pamphlets about Wallace.

In total, the four libel actions and two trials with all their associated costs and settlements had cost Wallace far, far more than the £500 he had hoped to get from an easy wager. Hampden, meanwhile, remained adamant that the world was flat.

გა

If it can be expensive to be right in theory, it can also prove costly when an experiment goes too well.

გა

Jones's perfect chimney

R.V. Jones is best known today for his brilliant technological achievements in the Second World War, in jamming German radio guidance during 'the Battle of the Beams', and for inventing methods of foiling radar with 'window' or 'chaff' as it is now called. Always a practical man, Jones liked his science to be on the experimental side and would often run impromptu experiments, such as the one he described in his wonderfully named article 'Impotence and Achievement in Physics and

Technology', which appeared in *Nature* magazine in 1965.

By his own admission Jones liked shooting things. In the article he recalled how, wandering through the old Clarendon Laboratory site in Oxford one day, presumably during the Second World War, he saw a large beaker full of dirty water and did what any red-blooded man would do. He unholstered his pistol and shot it, with surprising results. He noted that it was by no means the first beaker he had shot – something of an alarming revelation in itself – but whereas the others had simply shattered, this one had spectacularly exploded.

It didn't take a man of Jones's calibre long to work out the reason. Empty beakers would obviously just break when a bullet hit them, but this beaker had been full of water. As a dab hand in hydrostatics, Jones knew that whilst a gas would happily compress to allow for the presence of a bullet in the empty beaker, liquids were much less willing to perform the same trick. As the bullet had pierced the glass and entered the water, the water could not compress or get out of the way quickly enough, and so it had explosively shattered the glass.

By the time Jones was teaching hydrostatics at Aberdeen, this little experiment had become something of a class favourite and was soon known about outside the university classrooms. Indeed, it came to the attention of the local Territorial contingent of the Royal Engineers who always loved explosions and sometimes had a use for them. As it happened they were currently discussing how to demolish a local chimney, which they had been tasked with removing.

The traditional method would have been to slowly remove the bricks from one side at the base, propping the chimney up with wooden struts as they went, then setting fire to the struts to bring the whole thing down. Explosives could also be used but could be uncontrollable. Then there was Jones's experiment. What if the chimney base was filled with water and a small explosive charge detonated in it? Like the bullet in the beaker, the water would not be able to accommodate the explosion, forcing the bricks of the base outwards and bringing the chimney neatly to the ground.

They decided to give it a go. The great and the good of Aberdeen gathered one Sunday at the old paperworks to watch the novel demolition. The chimney was sealed up and filled with water to a height of 6 feet. A charge was lowered into the water and fired.

Often the most interesting results in science happen when things refuse to behave in the way you expect them to. This result was no different. At one level the experiment was a huge success – the charge blew and the water behaved exactly as it should, shooting outwards and taking out 6 feet of the bricks from all round the base of the chimney with it. But so symmetrical had the explosion been that the chimney appeared to hover in mid air for a moment before simply dropping down on top of the old foundations – still perfectly upright but now 6 feet shorter.

❧

Of course any scientist must roll with the blows, taking the failures along with the successes as part of the adventure. But sometimes history simply gets the wrong end of the stick, leaving you with fame of a wholly undeserved kind.

❧

Joseph Guillotin's act of kindness

There can be few machines in human history with a more terrible reputation than the guillotine, yet the man whose name it bears did not invent it. Indeed, he didn't even believe in capital punishment.

The decapitation apparatus now known as the guillotine was not a French invention, nor did it spring from the brain of Joseph

Guillotin. The origins of this macabre device are mediaeval, although the date of its first use remains uncertain. An early record comes from the town of Halifax in West Yorkshire, which by 1280 at the latest had the right to execute criminals. A contraption called 'The Halifax Gibbet' was first recorded as being used there in 1286 when one John Dalton was beheaded. A sixteenth-century engraving entitled 'The execution of Murcod Ballagh near to Merton in Ireland 1307' shows a similar machine, suggesting these were also in use across the Irish Sea. Scotland, not wishing to be left out, employed the 'Maiden', based on the Halifax Gibbet, to lop the heads off criminals from the minority of James VI in the late sixteenth century until its abolition in 1708.

Joseph Guillotin got caught up in its bloody history, strangely, through an attempted act of kindness. A doctor who had come to public prominence, he sat on a number of government committees. On 2 May 1789, during the early days of the French Revolution, he had become one of the ten deputies for Paris in the National Constituent Assembly. It was here, during a committee debate on capital punishment on 10 October, that he suggested that 'the criminal shall be decapitated; this will be done solely by means of a simple mechanism'.

This was not, however, an attempt to encourage execution – far from it, as Guillotin was opposed to the death penalty. As it very much existed, however, he determined that it should be made as fair, painless and private as possible.

At that time a person's social status in France made a great difference in how they might meet their death, should they be unfortunate enough to be found guilty of a capital offence. The poor might still find themselves 'broken on the wheel' – being beaten to death whilst attached to a revolving cartwheel – whilst the rich could nominate beheading and, given the choice, who wouldn't? Even then it was necessary for the relatives to bribe the headsman in an attempt to ensure the head was removed with a single blow and not slowly hacked off. The whole process would also take place in public in front of a jeering crowd and the relatives of the condemned. Guillotin reasoned that a decapitating machine would treat every victim equally, would never botch the job and could be placed out of public sight.

He recommended the use of this fairly common execution engine to a committee chaired by Dr Antoine Louis, which had been given the task of suggesting a practical device. They took their inspiration from the Halifax Gibbet and an Italian machine known as the Mannaia, as Louis states in his report to the Comité de Législation. The first actual guillotine was built by the German harpsichord-maker Tobias Schmidt and was first used on 25 April 1792.

Initially the machine was called a 'Louisette' or 'Louison' after the committee chairman Antoine Louis, but the name didn't stick. What had stuck in everyone's head by that point was a comic song that had appeared in the Royalist pamphlet *Actes des Apôtres*, which firmly associated Guillotin with the device. Thanks to his making one public comment, the man and the machine were made synonymous by the journalist Louis René Quentin de Richebourg de Champcenetz, who, ironically, was also to become one of its victims.

Joseph Guillotin himself had no idea that the coming 'Terror' (from 27 June 1793 to 27 July 1794) would bring his tentative suggestion to such horrific prominence but by that time everyone knew the device simply as the guillotine. Towards the end of the Terror, Guillotin himself was arrested and might have come face to face with the invention now unfairly bearing his name, were it not for Robespierre's fall from grace.

The humane doctor died in 1814, his heroic work – in saving lives as the first Frenchman to introduce Jenner's vaccination system – forgotten and his name instead for ever associated with a machine that took life. The last execution by guillotine in France took place on 10 September 1977.

8

Unpleasantness

(In which we come face to face with death,
murder, an odd form of suicide, angels, demons
and the awakened dead.)

Open up a few corpses: you will dissipate at once the
darkness that observation alone could not dissipate.

Marie-François-Xavier Bichat, *Anatomie générale*
appliquée à la physiologie à la médecine (1801)

Sometimes science can be very grim and rarely
more so than when dancing around the subject
of death. But let's take a look anyway . . .

✺

The real Frankenstein

The reason why Aloisio Luigi Galvani had a number of skinned
frogs' legs on his table has often been given as his wife's poor
health and her subsequent need for restorative frog soup. This
rather underestimates her involvement in one of the most important scientific discoveries of the eighteenth century.

Galvani and his wife Lucia Galeazzi were not, in fact, in the
soup game, but were actively involved in the study of a new
phenomenon. Galvani was Professor of Anatomy at the University
of Bologna. His particular research interest in the 1770s was the
effect of the recently discovered *fluido electrico* (electrical fluid)
on animal tissue. The couple did most of their work at home in
an improvised laboratory, using a selection of friction generators
and Leyden jars to test the effects of electricity on frogs.

One day, one of Galvani's assistants, very possibly Lucia, was
dissecting a frog's leg with a metal scalpel when a spark from
one of the generating machines jumped across just as the blade
of the scalpel touched an exposed nerve in the frog's leg. The
leg twitched, which was odd as dead frogs don't usually jump
around that much.

Galvani repeated the experiment and once more the dead leg
moved. He tried just touching the nerve with the unelectrified
scalpel and nothing happened. Next he attached a wire directly
between the nerve ending and his electrical generator – again
the muscle twitched. He tried again using silk, an insulator, and

the leg remained resolutely still. Clearly it was the 'electrical fluid' that was animating this otherwise dead tissue. Further experiments showed that this worked for living frogs as well as dissected muscles and other animals such as chickens.

It is uncertain why Galvani didn't immediately publish his work. Indeed, he waited until 1791 to do so, the year after his wife's death, but when he did publish, his book, *Commentary on the Effects of Electricity on Muscular Motion*, caused a sensation. For many it seemed that Galvani had discovered the secret 'spark' of life, the force that turns the inanimate into the animate. Demonstrations of 'Galvanism', as it was called, became a European craze with audiences thrilling to the dancing muscles of apparently dead and dissected creatures. But it was Galvani's nephew, Giovanni Aldini, who would take these experiments to their logical conclusion.

Aldini, himself Professor of Physics at the University of Bologna, was a great promoter of Galvanism, unlike the painfully diffident Galvani himself. He travelled Europe, demonstrating the effect in the most sensational of forms – reanimating dead humans. Of course, not many people would offer to be experimented on after death but, fortunately for Aldini, executed criminals had little say in the matter. Galvani himself had four times performed as anatomist in charge of the 'Carnival Anatomy' celebration in Bologna, in which an executed criminal was publicly dissected down to the skeleton in sixteen stages. On 17 January 1803, during a tour of Europe, Giovanni Aldini took this one step further.

That day he had gathered in a house near Newgate prison in London an audience made up of members of the Royal College of Surgeons. He set up his electrical discharge apparatus and the group then waited until the body of the unfortunate George Forster was brought into the room. Forster had come direct from Newgate where moments before he had hanged for the murder of his wife and child; indeed, his body was still warm.

Aldini stripped the corpse and began his experiments by touching copper poles attached to a Voltaic pile (a type of battery invented just three years previously by Alessandro Volta) to parts of the body, beginning around the mouth and ears. The audience witnessed the dead man's jaw quiver as electricity was applied. The face then suddenly contorted into a grimace and one dead eye opened. From here Aldini moved lower, making the fist clench and punch the air, and the chest heave. He finished by applying shocks to the dead man's rectum, at which the whole body began to writhe and 'dance', the back arching and the legs flailing around.

The effect of this demonstration on the audience was no less electric. Many there believed Forster was on the brink of being restored to life, whilst a Mr Pass, beadle to the Surgeons' Company, was said to have been so mortified by the sight that he died shortly afterwards. The *Newgate Calendar*, which reported crimes and executions, expressed its distress at the possibility that scientists might start reanimating criminals faster than the executioner could dispatch them, leading to all sorts of editorial problems. The editor, however, comforted himself with the thought that if a criminal was revived, he would have to be hanged again as the sentence of the court was very clearly that felons were to be hanged 'until dead'.

Aldini was himself always conservative in his claims. He never stated that he could bring a man back to life, but the story now had a life of its own. Other less honest demonstrators claimed they had restored dead, even decapitated, animals to life, and the image of dancing corpses haunted the European imagination. The monsters dreamt up there would finally find form fifteen years after the experiment on George Forster, in which a night-marish vision of Galvani's spark inspired Mary Shelley's gothic novel *Frankenstein*.

∾

Not that every scientist has waited for their
unwilling assistant to die . . .

∾

Last meals

At the beginning of the nineteenth century a debate still raged
in biology about what was known as 'spontaneous generation'.
Everybody knew where people came from, and cows, and other
large and easily visible animals, but what about parasites? How
did they get inside their hosts and how did they multiply? Many
considered that these were examples of a different way of repro-
ducing, known as 'spontaneous generation'. The idea was simply
that creatures like tapeworms naturally 'arose' from putrefying
matter, created by the decay itself. It sounds peculiar today but
it was an idea that would take over fifty years to prove wrong
and then in the most unethical of ways.

Friedrich Küchenmeister was a doctor with a particular
interest in human parasites, which added a whole new and unfortunate connotation to his name. In particular he was interested
in tapeworms: large parasites, sometimes up to 7 metres long
in the case of the pork tapeworm, which could infest the intestines of otherwise healthy people. The question was: where did
they come from? By the time Küchenmeister began his work, it
was already known that mature tapeworms produced eggs but
no one knew whether these eggs were responsible for producing
adult worms, nor where they went to do this, nor how they did
it in the first place. If adult tapeworms produced eggs, these
would be expelled in the host's faeces but as no one knowingly
ate faeces, how did these eggs get back into their human hosts?

Küchenmeister had a hunch, however. He had also done some

work on what were known as 'bladderworms', parasites found in the muscles of cows and pigs that lived in small cysts or 'bladders' in the flesh. These too apparently appeared out of nowhere but, strangely, when they were removed and examined under a microscope they bore an uncanny resemblance to tapeworms. It was this that gave Küchenmeister his great idea. Cutting out the living bladderworms from meat, he fed them to other animals and, having waited several days or weeks for them to 'incubate', he killed and cut open the animals to see whether they were now infested with tapeworms. They were. Küchenmeister began to suspect that bladderworms were just another stage in the life of the tapeworm.

Only one question now remained: were these bladderworms the cause of human tapeworm infestations? He had already noted that butchers often suffered tapeworm infections and had seen bladderworm cysts in pork that he had been served, so perhaps these unpleasant little creatures held the key? The only way to find out was to eat a cyst.

Some scientists are prepared to test their ideas out on themselves despite the obvious risks (see page 98), but Küchenmeister was not amongst them. He hit upon another brilliant idea. The prisons of his native Dresden often contained condemned criminals awaiting their date with the executioner. As they were going to die anyway, why not try out his theory on them first? The prison authorities agreed. A condemned woman was, for the five days before her execution, duly given several doctored meals prepared especially by Küchenmeister to contain eighty live bladderworms of three different species.

Two days after the unfortunate woman's death, he was allowed to perform an autopsy on the body and found a number of small tapeworms in her intestines, although other cysts appeared to have been partly digested. Considering he needed a longer incubation period, Küchenmeister managed to procure the unwilling services of another condemned man, feeding him live cysts from pig meat at four months and two and a half months before his death. When he finally received the freshly decapitated body on 31 March 1860, he was delighted to discover its intestines infested with adult tapeworms. He had been proved right.

Not everyone was quite as enthusiastic as Küchenmeister. Many in the medical establishment were horrified at the use in medical experiments of unconsenting condemned prisoners. Dr Alois Humbert was particularly incensed. He was been working on the same idea but had eaten the cysts himself and was assiduously searching his own excrement every day for evidence of adult tapeworms. In his noble insistence on trying his theory on himself, he had been beaten to the prize by just a few weeks.

∽

Fortunately not all scientists experiment on other people. Some simply make predictions about their own lives.

∽

Abraham de Moivre's deadly prediction

Abraham de Moivre was one of the greatest uncredited mathematicians of his age. Having escaped the persecution of Protestants in France, he moved to London where he rapidly established himself as a brilliant thinker, counting Edmund Halley and Isaac Newton (see page 24) amongst his friends. Indeed, de Moivre's voracious consumption of Newton's great mathematical work the *Principia* (which he read a page at a time as he walked along, having torn the pages from their binding) led Newton to answer the endless questions he received on his work by saying: 'Go to Mr De Moivre; he knows these things better than I do.'

Yet as a foreigner in England, de Moivre found it impossible to find the sort of permanent university post that would give him the space and time to develop his own ideas further. Instead he was forced to spend much of his life working as a impoverished private mathematics tutor, despite being a member of the Royal Society.

Despite these troubles, de Moivre made significant contributions to a number of fields, in particular as a pioneer of the study of probability in his 1718 book *The Doctrine of Chance*, although his intuitive analysis of games of chance and a gambler's probability of winning did nothing to improve his own financial situation.

What would improve the financial situation of many people in the City of London was his work on annuities, which outlined methods for calculating the cost of providing pensions based on mortality statistics and interest rates. Indeed, an estimation of mortality was to be de Moivre's final gift to mathematics.

At the age of eighty-seven, he noted that he was sleeping an extra ten to fifteen minutes each night. From this he calculated that when the accumulated extra time slept amounted to twenty-four hours, there would be no more time left in the day for him to sleep and he would die. This he duly did, that same year, on exactly the day his arithmetical progression predicted: 27 November 1754.

❧

Whilst others take a more active role in bringing that life to a dramatic conclusion.

❧

Jump

Occasionally amateur scientists have taken a great leap of faith, often at great personal risk, and in doing so have in a moment advanced science further than many years of dogged work would have done. They are the heroes of science, but one tale should go to show that they are also the exception.

Ever since the first sketch of the potentially lethal parachute was put to paper in the 1470s, everyone has agreed on one thing: the proper shape for a parachute is vaguely that of an umbrella – that is, the canopy is like an open umbrella above your head, trapping the air beneath it as it falls. Well, not quite everyone.

The gifted aerodynamicist Sir George Cayley had been fortunate enough to witness the first parachute jump ever made in Britain by André-Jacques Garnerin, who came to London in 1802 in a brief window of peace during the Napoleonic Wars to astound the people of the city with his feat of daring. And daring it was at that date, although not particularly unusual. Indeed, the first modern parachute jump had been made in 1783 by fellow Frenchman Louis-Sébastien Lenormand. Ever since, such reckless antics had been a nice money-earner for fairground owners who could find men willing to jump off high buildings when attached to nothing more than a sheet.

What Cayley noticed as Garnerin floated to earth, however, was that the parachute swayed wildly from side to side as the air spilt out from beneath the rim. He wondered whether inverting the canopy, so that the apex was at the bottom, making it a V shape rather than an inverted U shape, might not make for a more stable descent. These thoughts he wrote down in his seminal work *On Aerial Navigation*, where they were read by Robert Cocking who had also witnessed Garnerin's jump.

Cocking, then sixty-one, was a professional watercolourist but also a keen amateur scientist and he decided to put Cayley's ideas into action. Having constructed a V-shaped parachute, he persuaded the owners of the Vauxhall Gardens to lend him their huge balloon, *The Royal Nassau*, which was the only one available large enough to lift a crew, the parachute and Mr Cocking himself to a suitable height for the jump. Such a daring act would, naturally enough, also attract a huge crowd so the Vauxhall Gardens would make a handsome profit. There was, Mr Cocking informed the owners, no need for a preliminary trial.

On the evening of 24 July 1837, in front of a crowd of thousands, aeronaut Charles Green and his friend Edward Spencer lifted off in *The Royal Nassau* with Robert Cocking's parachute and the daredevil himself slung beneath them. The band played the national anthem.

From the start things did not go to plan. Despite the size of the balloon, it could not lift the heavy parachute fast enough. At just 5,000 feet, 3,000 feet lower than planned, Green shouted down to Cocking that they would have to make the jump now or abort before it got too dark. As Green himself later put it: 'Upon this Mr. Cocking said, "Then I shall very soon leave you".' It was a prescient comment. After a navigational check, Green continued:

I then asked him if he felt himself quite comfortable, and whether he found that the practical trial bore out the calculation he had made? Mr. Cocking replied, 'Yes; I never felt more comfortable or more delighted in my life.' Shortly afterwards Mr. Cocking said, 'Well, now I think I shall leave you.' I answered, 'I wish you a very good night and a safe descent, if you are determined to make it, and not to use the tackle [to get into the balloon's gondola with Green and Spencer].' . . . Mr. Cocking to this question made no other reply than 'Good night, Spencer; good night, Green.'

After an abortive attempt to disengage, the parachute finally fell away and the balloon, relieved of this huge weight, shot upwards 'with the velocity of a skyrocket'.

Two things now happened. First, Green and Spencer were forced to cling on to the floor of the basket and furiously vent gas from the balloon to prevent it exploding as it hurtled heavenwards. As the balloon was filled with coal gas – a mix of hydrogen, methane and carbon monoxide – this had the unfortunate side effect of blinding them and then knocking them out. When they came to, they managed to breathe from an airbag they had brought along to help with the altitude. This saved their lives. It is a matter of conjecture how high they got, as they were still blind at the highest point, but when Green got his sight back, well on the way down, the barometer suggested they were still at over 23,000 feet. They survived. Mr Cocking was less lucky.

The second part of the performance was just as dramatic and considerably more fatal. Whether the flaw in his plan dawned on him in his last moments we can never know, but Robert Cocking had forgotten to include in his calculations the weight of the parachute itself – an impressive 250 pounds (113.5 kilos), or ten times the weight of a modern parachute. It was this miscalculation that proved Cocking's undoing.

The crowd in the Vauxhall Gardens noted that he appeared to be descending in a very stable fashion but rather too quickly and that he seemed, if anything, to be accelerating rather than slowing. Moments later their suspicions were confirmed when the upper rim of the device was seen to collapse and the parachute began to break up. The machine, now looking like an umbrella blown inside out by the wind, continued to pick up speed. Three hundred feet from the ground, the basket was seen to detach. There followed a dull thud. Robert Cocking's broken body was found by farm labourers in a field near Lee in Kent.

There was, not surprisingly, an exhaustive inquiry into the sudden demise of Mr Cocking, and George Cayley's design was roundly condemned as the cause, blighting his reputation. In fact, more recent tests have shown that Cayley's inverted design can work rather well, provided the parachute is light and strong enough. Cocking's device was neither. The problem with instability in the traditional design was later overcome by the simple expedient of putting a small vent in the top of the chute to allow some of the air to escape.

ৎৎ

Amongst the more risk averse there has also been a tendency to try to use science to put off the evil day.

ৎৎ

Mithradates cheats death

Stories of ancient discoveries and inventions need to be taken with a pinch of salt, as they are often recorded by biased sources sometimes many centuries distant from the events they are describing. The one that has come down to us from ancient sources about this particular monarch is so unusual, however, that it might just have an element of truth.

Mithradates VI was not particularly popular. As king of Pontus, in modern-day Turkey, he was an autocratic ruler who had ruthlessly expanded his domain to cover nearly all of Asia Minor, much of the Black Sea coast and many of the Aegean islands. He had vied for power with the other aggressive states of the region, not least late Republican Rome, which claimed he had murdered 80,000 of its citizens and which fought repeatedly and bitterly against him. Nor was he always that well loved at home, having deposed and imprisoned his mother, killed his brother as well as several of his sons, and married his own sister. It is therefore perhaps not surprising that, like many of his ilk, he was a bit worried about being poisoned.

What marked Mithradates out from your average ruthless autocrat was that he intended to do something about the threat, beyond simply murdering anyone who looked annoyed with him. Sources agree that Mithradates was clever, some claiming he could speak all twenty-two languages of the nations he ruled, although he mainly used this talent to harangue them in their own tongue. He was also aware of Hellenistic advances in medicine, considering himself a descendant of Alexander the Great and hence an heir to the Hellenistic world. It was this claim to Greek scholarship that he intended to use to save his life.

First, Mithradates decided to do some research on poisons, sending out embassies to foreign countries, asking for details of deadly chemicals and their antidotes, and in return offering his own data. Thoughtfully he accompanied these bulletins with a batch of condemned prisoners so that his correspondents could try out the relevant toxins and cures in their arsenal without risking their own health. From this work he eventually derived a 'universal antidote', the Antidotum Mithradaticum, containing some thirty-seven ingredients including ginger and rhubarb. Pliny describes an even more complex concoction of fifty-four ingredients, which Mithradates took every day to proof himself against poison. A version of this 'Mithridate' was still being prescribed by London apothecaries as late as 1786.

These universal panaceas or 'theriacs' were obviously of limited use but one aspect of Mithradates's madness may well have had an effect, and it still bears his name. As well as taking antidotes, Mithradates practised Mithradatism – regularly consuming small, sub-lethal doses of known poisons in the hope of becoming immune to them: a process that can successfully be used to build up a tolerance to some toxins. Indeed, according to the Roman source Appian, a lifetime of taking poison to prevent himself being poisoned would finally rebound on the despot.

Having been defeated by the Roman general Pompey, Mithradates fled to Colchis to attempt to raise another army.

When his eldest son refused to help, he had him killed. His younger son threw caution to the winds and led a coup against him.

Mithradates decided to end it all rather than fall into the hands of the Romans and be paraded through the streets of Rome in triumph. So he ordered his entire harem and family to be poisoned, then swallowed the evil philtre himself, walking vigorously around to hasten its effect. But thanks to his Mithradatism, the drug worked on everyone except him. In the end he was forced to beg Bituitus, one of his guards, to run him through with his sword. Bituitus, never a man to ignore a direct order, duly obliged.

❦

Whilst fortunate enough not to have to resort to theriacs, some scientists have also been able to rely on a ministering guardian angel for protection.

❦

Gauss's saviour

Carl Friedrich Gauss was one of the greatest mathematicians who has ever lived, but he was not an easy man to get to know. In an era when discoveries were transmitted through the personal correspondence of scientists, he was a famously reluctant letter writer and, if provoked into writing, was terse and bad-tempered in his response. Only once did he ever write a warm letter, to a most unlikely correspondent, but then he did have to thank her for his life.

Sophie Germain, whilst also a brilliant mathematician, had been born in the late eighteenth century, when mathematics were considered so far beyond the capabilities of women as to make the very idea ridiculous. Fortunately, coming from a wealthy French family, she had access to her father's library, where she would find the inspiration both for her life's work and her saving of Gauss.

The book that changed her, and Gauss's, life was Jean-Étienne Montucla's *History of Mathematics*, a fairly straightforward work on the origins of the subject and its development from the days of the ancient Greeks onwards. What particularly inspired the young Sophie was the chapter on Archimedes, which retold the old story of how, during the Roman sacking of Syracuse, a soldier had burst into the great man's house to find him working on a mathematical problem. The soldier demanded that the mathematician come with him at once. Archimedes, an old man by this time, was so engrossed in his work that he ignored the young soldier who, a shade overexcited by the whole occasion, promptly killed him. Any subject that could inspire a man so much that he would be oblivious to the danger of approaching death, thought Sophie, sounded like one worth studying. She would become a mathematician.

The idea was not initially popular with her parents; indeed, to try to stop her spending her evenings poring over mathematical texts, her father removed her candles, wood for the fire and warm clothing. In response she hoarded candle stubs and worked late into the night wrapped in a blanket.

In 1794 she also enrolled in the École Polytechnique in Paris, which was quite an achievement as it was an institution for men only. Unable to attend in person, she took on the persona of a former student, the decidedly lacklustre Monsieur Auguste-Antoine Le Blanc, pretending he had returned to the establishment and having the course material sent to her under his name. Eventually her brilliant work came to the attention of Joseph-Louis Lagrange, the eminent mathematician supervising the course. He had noticed how Le Blanc had left as an idiot, but apparently returned to his studies as a mathematical genius. He demanded to meet the prodigy. Sophie's secret was out.

Luckily, most mathematicians don't care a jot whether a student is male or female, provided the work is good. That was exactly the attitude Lagrange took, even becoming Sophie's mentor. Sophie was soon deeply absorbed in number theory, in particular, working on partial solutions to Fermat's famously tricky 'Last Theorem'. This would of course involve corresponding with other experts in the field, and none was more revered than the great Gauss.

Gauss, however, as well as being known to be a miserable and rude correspondent, hated Fermat's Last Theorem, claiming it was irrelevant, possibly because he had had so little success with it himself. Thinking him unlikely to respond to a mere female, Sophie once again donned the mask of Monsieur Le Blanc. Surprisingly, Gauss did write back, probably because her suggestions for tackling the Fermat problem were as refreshing as they were excellent. Even so his tone remained a touch patronising and, of course, Sophie's identity remained hidden. It was only when the image of Archimedes came back into her mind that Gauss would discover her true identity.

It was 1806 and an apparently unstoppable Napoleon Bonaparte was storming through Prussia, taking city after city, like a latter-day Roman general. This got Sophie thinking. In one of those German cities was Gauss, a mathematician whom she considered the Archimedes of his age and who might easily become so absorbed in his work that an affronted soldier might lop off his head to teach him a lesson.

As luck would have it, the French general Joseph-Marie Pernety was a friend of Sophie's, so she pleaded with him to guarantee Gauss's safety. Having been made aware of the presence of this truculent genius in one of his conquered cities, Pernety sent word to find and protect the world's greatest mathematician, which was duly done. When Gauss appeared before the general, he was informed that he owed his life to Mademoiselle Germain, his correspondent. Gauss gratefully replied that he had never heard of her.

Finally Sophie Germain plucked up the courage to write once more to Gauss, this time, in her own name. He replied with possibly the only genuinely nice letter of his whole life:

> But how to describe to you my admiration and astonish-ment at seeing my esteemed correspondent Monsieur Le Blanc metamorphose himself into this illustrious personage who gives such a brilliant example of what I would find it difficult to believe. A taste for the abstract sciences in general and above all the mysteries of numbers is exces-sively rare: one is not astonished at it: the enchanting charms of this sublime science reveal [themselves] only to those who have the courage to go deeply into it. But when a person of the sex which, according to our customs and prejudices, must encounter infinitely more difficulties than men to familiarize herself with these thorny researches, succeeds nevertheless in surmounting these obstacles and penetrating the most obscure parts of them, then without doubt she must have the noblest courage, quite extra-ordinary talents and superior genius. Indeed nothing could prove to me in so flattering and less equivocal manner that the attractions of this science, which has enriched my life with so many joys, are not chimerical, [than] the predilection with which you have honoured it.

For several years the two corresponded, during which time Gauss inspired Sophie's further researches. His gratitude was not infinite, however, and when he moved to Göttingen and on to new subjects, his letters dried up. A year later Sophie abandoned mathematics for good.

Towards the very end of her life the two began writing again.

Gauss even tried to persuade his university to grant Sophie the degree she so richly deserved. Sadly she died, in 1831, whilst the gentlemen of the university were still, very slowly, pondering his request.

∾

Not everyone has had a guardian angel, however. Some of the finest minds have seemed beset by their own fatal demons.

∾

Galois's last stand

There are few more heart-rending stories in science than those of a gifted young life snuffed out before its time, although few of these tragic figures seem to have gone about their own destruction more wilfully than Évariste Galois.

Galois was not the sort of man to conform; indeed, he had been the rebellious type since childhood. Born in 1811, the son of a local mayor, Évariste spent his first twelve years being educated by his highly intelligent mother, but once at school he soon found his lessons boring and became what head teachers might describe as 'troublesome'. Whilst in his spare time he was already showing an astonishingly precocious talent for mathematics, in class his work remained lacklustre and, frankly, lazy.

In 1828 he applied to the École Polytechnique but, considering the mathematical entrance examination rather beneath him, which it probably was, he failed to explain his work properly in the oral examination and was refused entry. Maintaining a puzzling indifference to ambition, he enrolled in the École Préparatoire, a very junior school, instead. At least here his mathematical brilliance was noticed and he began publishing papers whilst still only sixteen. His main area of work was on the theory of polynomial equations and he was confident enough of his insights in this difficult area to submit papers to the Academy of Sciences.

What happened next, like so much in Galois's turbulent life, is hazy. For some reason, the referee appointed to read these papers, Augustin-Louis Cauchy, refused to accept them for publication. Undoubtedly Cauchy, a first-rate mathematician himself, realised the remarkable standard of the work and may well have returned it to Galois with the suggestion that he rework and combine the papers to be entered in the Academy's Grand Prize in Mathematics, which he very probably would have won.

Events were conspiring against Galois, however. In the July of that year, 1829, his father committed suicide after a political dispute with a local priest. Just two days later, Galois again attempted the examinations for the École Polytechnique, but was, for the second time, refused. No reason was given for the refusal but it seems likely that the troubled and troublesome Galois again failed to explain the details of his working to a mathematical examiner who was far his inferior in understanding of the subject. Faced with a tetchy and confusing explanation of work that the examiner simply didn't understand, he failed him.

Turning his back on the Polytechnique, Galois took the baccalaureate examination required for entry into the École Normale where he finally received his degree on 29 December 1829. Here too his fiery temperament and refusal to bow to authority would have unfortunate results. During the July Revolution of 1830, the director of the École Normale locked in his students to prevent them taking part in the riots that marked the abdication of Charles X and the accession of Louis-Philippe. When finally released, Galois immediately penned a savage critique of the director, which he sent to the *Gazette des*

Écoles. To absolutely no one's surprise, except perhaps that of Galois, he was expelled.

Nor was his academic career progressing outside the École. Early in 1830, before the revolution, he had again submitted his paper on polynomial equation theory to the Academy of Sciences but once again fate had intervened. The secretary who accepted the paper, Joseph Fourier, died before it was formally enrolled in the Grand Prix competition and the paper itself was lost.

No longer a part of an academic institution and rejected by the Academy – or so he believed, the turbulent Galois now joined a radical Republican artillery unit, only to find it almost immediately disbanded by a government that feared it might destabilise the delicate political situation. Nineteen of its officers were arrested but later acquitted. At the banquet to celebrate their release, the volatile Galois once more courted controversy by toasting Louis-Philippe with a dagger over his glass, suggesting to many an assassination threat against the king. The next day, and again to no one's surprise but his own, he was promptly arrested but was later released.

Having been acquitted of threatening the sovereign, a wiser man might have taken a low profile for a while but, the following Bastille Day, Galois was back at the barricades, this time leading a protest march, heavily armed and wearing his old artillery uniform. It was not only a clear provocation to the government but didn't immediately seem to serve any good purpose. He was, of course, arrested and this time received a six-month sentence.

In prison Galois did at least find some time to continue with his mathematics although as before this was tinged with disappointment. He had for a third time submitted his work on equation theory to the Academy but it was once more rejected, on this occasion by the mathematician Siméon-Denis Poisson, who, as you might have guessed, cited as the reason Galois's lack of clear explanation of his techniques. In response Galois swore to never darken the Academy's door again. He was true to his word.

Évariste Galois was released from prison on 29 May 1832. A month later he was dead. Like so much in Galois's life, the truth behind his last month is hard to come by. After his release he moved into a hostel, rather appropriately owned by a man called 'Motel', where he seems to have fallen in love with his landlord's daughter – Stéphanie-Felice Poterin du Motel. From the fragments of his letters that survive come suggestions that perhaps Galois was not the only man in Stéphanie's life and, somehow, he challenged that other suitor to a duel. The identity of his rival is in itself uncertain, and contemporary newspaper reports don't tally. There has even been some suggestion that the duel was a government plot to remove the troublesome mathematician, but there is no real proof of this.

All we know for sure is that on the night of 29 May 1832, Évariste Galois was convinced of two things. First, that he was going to die, and second, that this last evening was hence his only chance to leave behind some sort of academic testament.

He did not sleep that night but stayed up, gathering together, annotating and rewriting elements of his work, which he then set out, in his usual chaotic fashion, in a letter to his old teacher, Auguste Chevalier. Contained within the notes were the basis for a whole new area of mathematics – now called Galois theory – along with numerous other insights, many of which would not be understood until many years later. The twentieth-century mathematician Hermann Weyl would comment: 'This letter, if judged by the novelty and profundity of ideas it contains, is perhaps the most substantial piece of writing in the whole literature of mankind.'

The next morning at dawn, Galois went to his duel where he received a fatal wound to the abdomen. He died the following day, aged just twenty.

❧

To be fair, not every murderous encounter in
science leads to the death of a genius.
Sometimes the scientist wins. And gets away
with it. And finds in it the inspiration for
another moment of genius. Sometimes.

❧

Muybridge's moving target

Edward Muggeridge was an unusual man. Born in Kingston-upon-Thames in Surrey, England, he emigrated to New York in the mid-nineteenth century, changing his name, for reasons that are still not entirely clear, to Eadweard Muybridge. He initially set up in business as a book importer before moving his company to what he hoped would be the more lucrative territory of San Francisco, then in the grip of the Californian Gold Rush. A life selling books would have lain ahead, were it not for a near-fatal stagecoach accident in Texas after which his doctor, the eminent Sir William Gull (a sometime suspect in the Jack the Ripper murders), suggested he adopt a more outdoor lifestyle to aid his convalescence.

During the early 1860s, Muybridge travelled extensively from the US to England and Europe. It was during a stay in his old home town of Kingston that he was taught the art that would change his fortunes. In the US he had befriended an early daguerreotypist, Silas Selleck, and become fascinated with how these fixed images preserve a moment in time. Daguerreotypes were one-offs and could not be copied, whereas the technique that Arthur Brown taught him in England – wet-plate 'collodion' photography – produced negatives from which you could make as many prints as you liked.

By 1866, Muybridge was back in San Francisco and working with Selleck, offering the American public something new – collodion prints of the extraordinary landscapes of their young nation. His views of the Old West, its burgeoning cities and endless vistas, quickly earned him a reputation. In 1872, the former governor of California and president of the Central Pacific Railroad, Leland Stanford, selected him to solve an age-old puzzle.

There are many stories about the nature of Leland Stanford's commission. The most famous, and apocryphal, version has it that it was the result of a $25,000 bet between the great man and his friend Fred MacCrellish, proprietor of the *Alta California* newspaper, over whether at any point all four hooves of a trotting horse were off the ground at the same time. Exciting as the story is, there is no evidence that either Stanford or Fred MacCrellish ever laid a bet in their lives. Bet or no bet, however, the question remained the same: did a moving horse ever have all four hooves off the ground at once?

Muybridge set about answering this question in two ways. First, he had to find a way of recording an image quickly – so quickly that the movement of a horse would appear to have stopped. Second, he had to trigger the camera at exactly the right moment to capture each part of the horse's gait. The first problem he solved by hanging white sheets behind the view of the camera and recording only the silhouette of the passing animal. The second was solved for him by a railroad employee who built for him an electrical trigger that could be attached to a tripwire.

So in May 1872, Muybridge began taking photographic silhouettes of Stanford's prize racehorse Occident as it trotted past his camera. After several passes Muybridge finally got the image he wanted and could answer the question. In a trot there was a moment when none of the horse's hooves were touching the ground.

And that might have been the end of Eadweard Muybridge's contribution to science, were it not for his unfortunate appearance in the dock at a murder trial. Following the birth of his son in 1874, Muybridge discovered that his wife was having an affair with an English drama critic, George 'Harry' Larkyns, who was probably also the true father of the child. Muybridge dealt with this emotional catastrophe in a particularly decisive way. Approaching Larkyns on 17 October at Calistoga in California, he announced: 'Good evening, Major, my name is Muybridge. Here is the answer to the message you sent my wife.' With that he shot the man dead.

At his trial for murder Muybridge pleaded insanity. Several witnesses testified to the fact that his personality had changed considerably for the worse after his Texan accident, but the jury threw out the plea. It was not that they had taken against him; in fact they thought Larkyns had got exactly what he deserved. Instead they returned a verdict of 'justifiable homicide'. Muybridge walked free and headed off for a long tour of Central America, far from the prying eyes of journalists. 'His' unfortunate son was placed in an orphanage.

When Muybridge returned to California in 1876 he was again enthused with photography and the following year accepted funding from Stanford to continue his experiments photographing horses at the magnate's Palo Alto stud farm. With cash in the bank, Muybridge now began to develop his technique, placing twelve cameras on a rail in a 15-metre-long shed, facing a white-painted background marked off with vertical numbered lines. The cameras, which could produce shutter speeds of a thousandth of a second, were each attached to an electric trigger via a tripwire, enabling them to capture the whole of the horse's gait at one pass (previously he had taken just one image per pass). Later this apparatus was extended to twenty-four cameras, all of which fired consecutively in the space of a single second.

These images were published in 1878 in the book *The Horse*

in Motion. That same year the editor of *Scientific American* magazine theorised that Muybridge's photographs would be even more effective if placed in a zoetrope, a children's toy that used a series of consecutive images in a rotating drum to give the illusion of movement.

Muybridge seized on the idea, creating what he called the Zoöpraxiscope, which he demonstrated in Paris in 1881 before heading off on a lecture tour of the learned societies of London. As the first person ever to demonstrate photographic motion pictures, he was perhaps the founder of the movie business and was widely fêted, *The Illustrated London News* commenting that his wonderful device was like 'a magic lantern run mad'.

On the verge of moving back to his home country, Muybridge received news that his old sponsor, Leland Stanford, had published a book, written by one Dr J.B. Stillman, a little surprisingly titled *The Horse in Motion,* which was illustrated by drawings taken from Muybridge's photographs. However, there was no mention of Muybridge's name anywhere in the book. It is not known why Stanford chose to do this but, outrageously, he had. Muybridge was accused of plagiarism and forced to return to the States.

Back in America, he began work on a monumental publication with a no less monumental title: *Animal Locomotion, an electrophotographic investigation of consecutive phases of animal movement, 1872–1885,* which restored his reputation worldwide, although at eleven volumes with 2,000 images of humans, birds and animals, very few copies were ever sold. Perhaps more importantly for what came later, in 1893 he also demonstrated his Zoöpraxiscope to the paying public in the specially built and impossibly named Zoöpraxographical Hall at the Chicago World's Columbian Exposition, making that hall the world's very first cinema.

In 1894, Muybridge finally returned to his native Kingston

where he died from a heart attack ten years later, while, for reasons that can now only be guessed at, vigorously excavating a miniature replica of the Great Lakes in his garden. He was seventy-four.

❧

Then again there are also those who
use their scientific knowledge for calculated,
premeditated murder.

❧

Dr Buchanan's fatal mistake

A good knowledge of chemistry is an excellent addition to the arsenal of any would-be murderer and it is precisely this that has given some doctors over the years a belief that they could, using their pharmaceutical skills, commit the perfect crime.

That was certainly the view of Dr Robert Buchanan, who in 1892 was pondering a series of difficult questions. He had married Anna Sutherland, a wealthy brothel-keeper in New York. It was not perhaps the sort of match made by many well-to-do doctors of the day but Anna was rich and Robert Buchanan needed a lot of money, as he preferred the clubs and bars of the city to the doctor's surgery where he might earn some cash for himself.

However, he found Anna's manner coarse and grating, as you might perhaps expect from a tough New York brothel-keeper, and worse still it was not always easy to get money out of her. Then there was his first wife, Helen, whom he had divorced but who now – in comparison to his new, mean madame – seemed like a rather better bet and whom he was hoping to marry again. The solution to all his problems seemed simple: murder. If he could kill Anna, he'd inherit her $50,000 fortune and be free to marry Helen.

In mid-April 1892, Anna fell sick and, with her husband at her side, she died, just a few days later on the 22nd of that month. Another doctor was called to certify the cause of death and he examined the body, declaring Anna to have died from a brain haemorrhage, which was all rather convenient. Buchanan inherited her $50,000 and moved back to his native Nova Scotia where, just three weeks after Anna's death, he remarried his first wife.

And there the story would have ended, were it not for the late Anna's former partner. He was alarmed to hear of her death and was even more surprised to learn that she had left him nothing in her substantial will. To him it looked suspicious, misgivings that he passed on to Ike White, a reporter for the *New York World*. When White followed up the story, he was immediately shocked to find that Buchanan had left for Canada and had already remarried.

Going to Anna's brothel, he began interviewing the staff. Here he learnt a lot more about Buchanan's habits and, in particular, an incautious boast he had made two years previously. At that time one Carlyle Harris was on trial for the murder of his wife and the story was all over the newspapers. That it was indeed murder had been concluded from an examination of Mrs Harris's body, whose pinpoint pupils definitively proved that she had been poisoned with morphine. As Buchanan chatted to the girls about the case, he called Harris a 'stupid amateur' and commented that he wouldn't have made such an elementary mistake.

This comment interested White. He tracked down a former employee who had been there on the night of this conversation, who added further information. Buchanan had actually explained that what Harris should have done is put belladonna drops in his wife's eyes before she died, as this would have made the pupils dilate. Then no one would have suspected poisoning.

When White interviewed the nurse who had attended Anna in her last days, she remembered Dr Buchanan leaning over his wife and putting something in her eyes.

When Ike White broke the story in the *New York World*, it proved a sensation. The authorities had little choice but to exhume the corpse of Anna Sutherland, which was discovered to contain at least 300 milligrams of morphine – a fatal dose.

Robert Buchanan was arrested and on 20 March 1893 stood trial for his wife's murder. It would prove to be one of the first great forensic cases fought in a US court, with a host of expert witnesses being called to discuss both the effects of morphine poisoning and the effects on that of administering atropine (the alkaloid found in belladonna). The *New York Times* commented during the trial that the science was so complex that the jury would 'have to sit and listen to lawyers and witnesses whose talk will all be remote from the subjects to which any but scientific men ever give consideration'.

Nor was there simply to be talk. In a gruesome opening flourish, the prosecution brought a cat into court, which was injected with a fatal dose of morphine. The contracted pupils were noted before atropine was introduced into the dying creature's eyes to demonstrate how this reversed the effect.

Buchanan's lawyer, a former doctor himself, responded brilliantly in cross-examining the prosecution's chief toxicologist, setting up his own grisly, if rather amateur, experiment to show that the Pellagri test, used to detect morphine in Anna's body, could produce a false positive just using rotting flesh. In other words, forensic evidence from Anna's decayed corpse could not be relied upon as indicating that she had died from morphine poisoning.

For a while it appeared that Buchanan might get away with it. In fact, it would not be the science but his own mouth that would condemn him. His lawyers made the fatal mistake of putting him in the dock, where his self-serving, highly inconsistent and contradictory evidence convinced the jury of his guilt. On 2 July 1895, Dr Robert Buchanan died in the same electric chair at Sing Sing that had executed 'amateur' poisoner Carlyle Harris just two years earlier.

∽

In case this is all sounding too
sinister, we should finish this chapter
with someone who never hurt a fly but who
managed to go on making great discoveries
even after his own death.

∽

Seeing through Dalton's eyes

John Dalton saw many things in a wholly new light but it would be his eyes themselves that finally gave science an insight into the observation that set Dalton on a lifetime of discovery.

John Dalton is best remembered today for advancing atomic theory. He was not the first to suggest that all matter might be made up of tiny, fundamental building blocks, although he revolutionised chemistry by positing that these 'atoms' of each element were made of the same stuff, differing only in mass. The idea of atomic weight was a brilliant insight, enabling chemists to begin to explain how elements interacted to form new compounds, as later elegantly displayed in Berzelius's 'H_2SO_4' style notation and ultimately in Mendeleev's Periodic Table of elements (see page 84), the predecessor of which had first been drawn up by Dalton himself.

But it was Dalton's first published work and his last bequest that perhaps give us the best insight into the mind of this poor weaver's son who would change the world. Dalton had been sent out to work aged just ten but had even then a love of knowledge that would more than make up for so short a formal education. As a young schoolmaster, he as much taught himself as his classes and, thanks to his fellow Quakers, in 1794 he became Professor of Mathematics at the recently created Nonconformist Manchester Academy.

It was here that he made his first curious observation. In truth he had for some time known that he had something a shade odd about him. As a Quaker he was expected to dress soberly but occasionally he caused some alarm at Friends' meetings by turning up in dazzlingly bright clothes. Nor did he restrict this eccentric dress sense to his own wardrobe, buying his elderly mother bright-scarlet stockings for one birthday.

What bothered Dalton was flowers, in particular pink flowers or, as he called them, blue flowers. Astonishingly, although people must for centuries have disagreed about what colour something was, no one had come up with a coherent idea of why or, indeed, even noted that this was the case. Perhaps because we assume that the colours we see as red or blue or yellow are what other people call red or blue or yellow, we don't ask the deeper question: is it that particular colour? Dalton did ask it and soon realised that, not only did he see things differently from others, it must be due to some failing in his eyesight.

He laid out his results in his first ever published work, *Extraordinary Facts Relating to the Vision of Colours, with Observations*, in which he noted: 'That part of the image which others call red, appears to me little more than a shade, or defect of light; after that, the orange, yellow and green seem *one* colour, which descends pretty uniformly from an intense to a rare yellow, making what I should call different shades of yellow.'

Dalton could only guess at what caused this malfunction, as he could hardly dissect his own eyes. So for the time being, he surmised that the problem might be due to the aqueous humour (the thick, watery substance that fills the interior of the eye) being tinted and so absorbing some colours of light. Ever the investigator, however, he asked that his eyes should be removed when he had no further use for them, after his death, and dissected to find out what exactly was going on.

John Dalton died on 27 July 1844 as one of the most celebrated scientists of the era. He had even been presented at court, an event that had accidentally led to another dazzling display. As a Quaker and therefore a pacifist, Dalton could not attend court in the traditional garb, which included a ceremonial sword, so he chose to wear the only acceptable alternative, his bright-scarlet academic gown or, as he saw it, his sober blue gown.

After his death 40,000 people filed past his body in Manchester Town Hall before a funeral procession 2 miles long took him to his final resting place. But he went there, as he had requested, without his eyes. They were back in the laboratory where his strong-stomached assistant, Joseph Ransome, was about to investigate Dalton's first and last problem.

Ransome cut a hole in one eyeball and squeezed out the liquid, proving instantly that Dalton's own theory was wrong – the aqueous humour was perfectly clear. He then cut a hole in the back of the other eye and had a look through it to see whether there was any other obstruction or discolouration of the lens that caused the colour blindness, but again nothing seemed amiss. Convinced that there was nothing physically wrong with Dalton's eyes, Ransome preserved them in a bottle and put them away, waiting for later, wiser generations to address the mystery.

Over the following century, Dalton's realisation that some people could not see certain colours had become so mainstream that in some countries the condition was called Daltonism. Furthermore it was now also understood that the problem was caused by malfunctioning colour receptors (cones) in the retina at the back of the eyeball and that it was genetic. Dalton himself had partially guessed at this when he recorded that his brother saw colours exactly as he did, although the exact type of Daltonism from which Dalton suffered was still a matter of conjecture.

Thanks to Ransome's careful preservation of his eyes, however, the answer could finally come from a DNA analysis. In 1995 it was announced that a sample of Dalton's eye had shown that he suffered from deuteranopia: in other words, he lacked the middle-wavelength cones. One hundred and fifty-one years after his death, Dalton finally had the answer to his first question.

9

Frauds, Fools and Fibbers

(In which we meet some scientists behaving badly and some badly behaved people pretending to be scientists.)

If once a man indulges himself in murder, very soon he comes to think little of robbing; and from robbing he comes next to drinking and sabbath-breaking, and from that to incivility and procrastination.

Thomas de Quincey, 'On Murder Considered as One of the Fine Arts' (Supplementary Paper), *Blackwood's Magazine* (November 1839)

Not everything in science is heroic and
it would be wrong not to include some of the
less illustrious stories from its annals in this
book. But let's start with someone who didn't
want to fool anyone but who just believed
too much himself.

Bernard's rancid omelette

There are probably a great many things you can do with 2,000 eggs but making gold isn't one of them. This apparently self-evident fact was not enough to put off one alchemist.

Bernard of Treviso is a shadowy character, as many from the fifteenth century are, but his obscurity is compounded by the fact that he may actually be more than one person and although he's called Bernard of Treviso, as far as anyone can tell, he – or possibly they – came from Padua.

However, this is the least of our confusions when it comes to the life and works of Bernard. Bernard was, as far as we know, born into a wealthy family around 1406 but from early youth clearly showed an interest in furthering his family's fortune by means of alchemy. Having studied works of the early Arabic (or possibly Persian) chemist and alchemist, Abu Musa Jabir ibn Hayyan al azdi (known in the West as Geber), he set out to discover the Philosopher's Stone, a legendary substance that would turn base metals into gold. We may wonder why he felt the need to do this as he was rich enough never to need to work but perhaps it was simply the academic interest that drove him. In any case, as the years went by and his attempts failed, a certain economic priority did return to his life.

The problem for alchemists, then as now, was that they tended to attract charlatans whose aim was to lure away a large chunk of an alchemist's remaining resources and turn them, not into gold but into vague promises of help or hints towards a conclusion that was always just out of reach. So it was with Bernard. One nineteenth-century source claims he attracted 'helpers' like bees, most of whom simply fleeced the poor man before setting him to work on ever more unlikely chemical plans, one of which alone involved twelve years of chemical distillation and cost 6,000 crowns.

Eventually even Bernard lost faith and, tiring of local 'help', decided to travel, in search of a new breakthrough. It is perhaps here that Bernard could really have made his mark, as long-distance journeys in the fifteenth century were reasonably unusual. His trip through Belgium, France, Britain, Turkey, Rhodes, Palestine, Persia, North Africa and Egypt must have made him one of the best-travelled men of his day. Yet it was not the journey that interested Bernard. Meeting with a Cistercian monk, Master Geoffrey Leuvrier, he believed for a while he had found a true fellow alchemist.

Geoffrey thought that the secret of the Philosopher's Stone probably involved hens' eggs – lots of hens' eggs – although he couldn't really explain why. What he did do was get Bernard to buy 2,000 of them, just in case he was right. The process required that the eggs be hard-boiled and peeled, and the shells calcified in a fire. After the yolks had been separated from the whites, both whites and yolks had to be mixed with horse dung and left to putrefy. This stinking mass was then strained and distilled time and time again to produce a 'red and white water'. In total the experiment took a full eight years. The result proved to be simply rancid egg-and-dung juice.

Bernard, now on the alchemical rebound, next fell in with an absolute charlatan, a protonotary in Bruges who claimed that not only had he already made the Philosopher's Stone but he could do it again (given enough of someone else's money and time). After a year's work, again with eggs but also this time with vinegar, all Bernard had to show for his efforts was a pickled egg and a high fever that nearly killed him.

Bernard, by now broken both in health and fortunes, was forced to sell his Italian estates. With what little he had left he retired to Rhodes, which he had previously visited on his grand tour and clearly taken a fancy to. It was said that shortly before his death he met a priest on the island who finally confided in him the secret of making gold, but for Bernard it came too late.

However, for several hundred years after his death (around 1490), it was said that this secret could be found in very expensive editions of his attributed writing. There were also many who claimed to have met Bernard on his travels and who could pass on the secret to you – at a price.

❧

If Bernard was honest but gullible,
then Princess Lotus Blossom, had she lived 400
years earlier, would have been just the sort of
dishonest acquaintance to spin him a yarn.

❧

Princess Lotus Blossom

Anyone bumping into Princess Lotus Blossom as she toured the USA in the early years of the twentieth century might have been forgiven for thinking they were meeting an exotic Oriental lady, whose preparations of 'Tiger Fat' and 'Vital Sparks' offered the ordinary American the chance to experience the wonders of ancient Chinese medicine. This was not, in all honesty, the case.

Princess Lotus Blossom was not all she seemed. In reality she was Violet McNeal, a sixteen-year-old farm girl from the Midwest who had run away to the Twin Cities of Minneapolis and St Paul, and married Will, a patent-medicine quack. Actually, that too was not quite true as the 'ceremony' they had gone through was also a fake. In the course of their lives together she never even found out his real surname. What was true was that he was a violent, opium-addicted charlatan and Violet was soon introduced to both the patent-medicine business and the drug.

At the St Louis World's Fair of 1904 she first emerged as a Chinese princess, guardian of the medical secrets of the Far East. Thanks to the Chinese Exclusion Act of 1882, which banned Chinese immigration for ten years, a whole industry in fake-Chinese travelling salesmen had grown up. Violet skilfully combined the patter of those fraudulent Orientals with some stage magic, together with the usual range of patent 'medicines', repackaged not as 'Indian cures', as was then common, but as Chinese miracle cures. She would appear on stage dressed in a Mandarin coat and skullcap and tell the audience an extraordinary tale from her 'homeland' – something she knew they could never verify.

What she told them was that a strange disease had made all the men of China impotent. Faced with national disaster, the emperor had offered a fortune to anyone who could devise a cure. Fortunately, there was one man who could. The sage He Tuck Chaw had been travelling in a remote volcanic region of the country when he had stumbled upon a species of turtle in which the females outnumbered the male by a thousand to one. Clearly the male held the secret of astonishing virility, which He Tuck Chaw finally isolated as coming from a small 'pouch' – the Quali Quah pouch – at the base of the animal's brain. By removing and powdering this, he was able to make a medicine that would forever leave Viagra in the shade. He presented this to the emperor, who ordered the men of China each be given a tiny portion. Sure enough, their virility was instantly restored.

Princess Lotus Blossom confided in her audience that she too had that secret ingredient, which she had made into 'Vital Sparks' pills, so that American men could enjoy the same vigour (not that they needed it, of course). For women or those with other ailments, she could also offer her 'Tiger Fat', which was, of course, the Orient's other greatest medical secret.

After each successful show Violet and her 'husband' would retire to their hotel where they would make up the next batch of their cures. 'Tiger Fat' was made in a bucket by mixing petroleum jelly, camphor, eucalyptus oil, turpentine and menthol with a bit of paraffin.

'Vital Sparks' pills were even easier. Whilst Violet was performing – Will always made Violet do the work – he would go and buy a pound of small, round, boiled sweets known as 'buckshot candy'. These would be put in a drawer in their room, dampened with water and sprinkled with some bitter aloe. Will would then run the drawer in and out a few times to cover them evenly. Put in boxes, these boiled sweets became the magical restorer of American virility. With only confidence lacking in many of the eager male customers, the placebo effect alone could be left to do its job. Many men agreed that 'Vital Sparks' were the miracle of their day.

Some scientific frauds are considerably more sophisticated than buckshot candy and, where an audience really wants to believe, it's astonishing what a quick-witted fraudster can get away with.

The mechanical Turk

Since the invention of the machine, few ideas have fascinated inventors and scientists more than that of making one that could actually think. The creation of a machine as complex as the human mind – a machine that might become aware – is still the ultimate goal of students of Artificial Intelligence, but the challenge is formidable. Of course one can always cheat.

Perhaps the most celebrated AI fraud began surprisingly early, around 1769, when Baron Wolfgang von Kempelen was visiting the Empress Maria Theresa of Austria at the Schönbrunn Palace. As was usual in palaces, some entertainment had been laid on, in this case an illusionist who impressed everyone – with the exception of Kempelen. Whether it was the magnificence of his surroundings, the imposing presence of the empress or just a shade too much claret, he announced that the illusions were mere trifles and he would return with something far more impressive. And to his great credit, he did. Partly.

The following year Kempelen unveiled a mechanical wonder – a life-sized model of the head and upper body of a man seated at a square box on which stood a chess set. The bearded figure, dressed in Ottoman robes and a turban, held in his left hand a long Turkish smoking pipe. Not surprisingly, it was known simply as 'The Turk'. What was truly amazing about this peculiar automaton was that it played chess – really rather well.

Kempelen, who was something of a showman, would demonstrate his marvel by first removing certain panels on the machine and asking his audience to come and inspect. As they peered inside they could wonder at the complex clock-work cogs and gear chains whirring away. By removing the front and back panels, Kempelen could even let his audience look right through the apparatus to prove there was simply machinery inside. With everyone satisfied that this was nothing more than a very elaborate clock, it was time for the miracles to begin.

First, Kempelen would challenge anyone in the room to play the Turk at chess. When he had a taker, the game would start and the Turk would apparently come alive. Its left hand would rise from the cushion on which it normally rested, take a white piece and move it. If it put its opponent's queen in check, it would gravely nod its head twice (three times if it was the king). Should its opponent fancy a chat during the match, the Turk could even converse in any one of three languages via a pegboard on which it marked out answers to questions.

As the match proceeded, Kempelen would be darting around the room, encouraging the audience to come forward and inspect the workings or to hold magnets close to the Turk to prove it wasn't a magnetic trick. From time to time he would also peer into a mysterious small box that he had placed on the machine as though something inside controlled the game. Games were usually short, averaging around half an hour, and the Turk almost always won. After its victory, Kempelen would take a metaphorical lap of honour by getting his marvel to perform the 'Knight's Tour' – a complex puzzle requiring a single knight to cover every square on the board once without repetition.

To the audience in the Schönbrunn Palace, and on its subsequent excursions around Europe, it seemed astonishing. The mechanical movement alone of the Turk was impressive enough but its brilliant chess skills and eerie ability to communicate through its pegboard was astounding. The greatest minds queued up to challenge the Turk, unable to believe it could be that good. The best player in France, François-André Philidor, actually beat it although he later admitted it was the most exhausting game of his life. After Kempelen's death its new owner arranged matches with Napoleon Bonaparte and Benjamin Franklin (see page 28) – both of whom it defeated. By this date it had also had a voice box installed so that the mechanical Turk could intone 'Échec' when it placed its opponent in check.

Of course not everyone believed in the machine. Some suggested that its human abilities might have a lot to do with it being somehow controlled by a human. Nevertheless, the Turk outlived Kempelen and, under new management, continued to impress audiences until it was finally destroyed in a fire in 1854.

All was indeed not what it seemed and it began to be said that the machine's human abilities implied that inside it there was – a human. Shortly after, the son of the last owner decided to come clean, publishing a series of articles in *The Chess Monthly* revealing the secret.

Inside the Turk a human (known as 'the director') sat on a movable seat. When Kempelen, or a later owner, was about to open one of the inspection doors, the director would slide himself out of sight, covering his position with panels of fake clock-work machinery. When the game was actually played, each chess piece contained a strong magnet, which attracted another magnet under each square, allowing the director to make out from the inside where all the pieces were. The positions were then trans-ferred on to a pegboard, to keep him informed as to how the game was progressing. The pegboard was in turn connected to a pantograph needle whose movements over the board were translated mechanically into the movements of the Turk's arm. Finally, in order to see what was going on, the director had a candle that sat under a chimney venting out of the top of the Turk's turban.

It was an astonishing feat for the poor 'director' but one for which they could never take any credit. That went in its entirety to Kempelen, ensuring that his (somewhat tarnished) reputation would live on and hence proving the epitaph on his tomb to be true: 'Non omnis moriar . . .' or 'I will not die completely'.

~∞~

Then there are those cases where not only is it
uncertain whether the promised 'science' is real
but even whether the perpetrator themselves
actually believes it to work.

~∞~

N-rays

The 'undiscovery' of 'N-rays' is a startling example of how good scientists can come to very wrong conclusions.

The original discovery of N-rays was broken to the world media in 1903 by the distinguished French physicist René Prosper Blondlot. He had been attempting to polarise another recently discovered mystery ray, the X-ray, and in the process had noticed what he thought was a change in the brightness of an electrical spark placed in the line of the X-ray beam. This, he hypothesised, must be due to another new ray, which he christened the N-ray after the university where he worked, at Nancy.

At this time new rays seemed to be coming along almost every day, so it did not exactly make headline news, but such a result needed independent proof. Soon a large number of physicists in France and elsewhere were experimenting on generating N-rays and studying their properties.

The initial results were encouraging. With over 120 scientists working on the phenomenon, and a dozen papers appearing on the subject that year, it seemed that French science had triumphed. Experiments by some of France's most famous scientists showed that N-rays were not only produced by X-ray sources but could emanate from a huge range of substances, including gases, magnetic fields and various chemicals, as well as, rather surprisingly, the human nervous system.

As research continued apace, a committee of the French Academy of Sciences, chaired by Henri Poincaré (see page 61), awarded Blondlot its prestigious 20,000-franc Leconte prize. Other physicists, keen to bathe in the glow of academic and national approval, even made bids to claim priority over Blondlot for the discovery.

But outside France the scientific community was not happy, most particularly in Cambridge, where, in the autumn of 1904, the British Association for the Advancement of Science was meeting. A number of physicists there were concerned at their abject failure to reproduce the results that were flooding out of France. Why was it only the French who could find N-rays? As it happened, amongst those in Cambridge that autumn was the American physicist Robert Wood, famed for his work debunking dubious theories. Many years later he recorded what had been decided at that meeting. Whilst the intervening years have led to some elaboration of the plot, his notes provide one of the most conclusive and damning disproofs in scientific history.

According to Wood, he was prevailed upon to go to France, to Professor Blondlot's laboratory, where the discoverer of N-rays was, apparently, only too pleased to demonstrate the proof of his find. Arriving in Nancy, Wood was taken to the professor's laboratory. Blondlot first showed him a card on which some circles had been painted in luminous paint. He dimmed the gaslight in the laboratory and switched on his N-ray source. With a sense of awe he asked Wood to observe how the card glowed brighter when in the N-ray beam. Wood couldn't see any difference but was told his eyes were insufficiently sensitive to register the change.

Keen to have some empirical evidence, Wood asked whether he could move a lead screen in and out of the path of the ray, out of sight of Blondlot, whilst Blondlot watched the card and from its glow announced whether the N-rays were on or off.

This Blondlot agreed to do but got mostly wrong. Wood, not yet in possession of conclusive proof, bit his tongue.

The most impressive evidence for the existence of N-rays was said to come from a piece of apparatus Blondlot had designed, which he would now demonstrate.

The N-ray spectroscope was like an optical spectroscope but the lenses and prism in it were made of aluminium. Blondlot took a vertical thread coated with luminous paint and moved it in and out of a narrow beam of N-rays supposedly being emitted by the device. As the thread crossed the line of the N-rays, it brightened, or so Blondlot maintained. As the position at which the thread brightened could be measured and was always the same, this had been taken by many as proof of the existence of the mysterious ray.

In the dark of the room Blondlot performed his experiment, announcing when the thread brightened. Wood took advantage of the darkness to remove the vital aluminium prism from the apparatus without Blondlot noticing. He then asked for a repeat performance. Once again Blondlot claimed to see the thread brighten in the path of the N-rays, even though one vital component of the experiment was in Wood's pocket.

Wood slipped the prism back but by now the French professor's assistant, who had been closely observing Wood, was suspicious. After the apparatus was reset, the assistant prepared to make an observation. In the dark Wood made clumsy noises as though tampering with the apparatus, whilst in fact not touching it. When the assistant looked for the magical rays, he announced to Blondlot in French (which he didn't think Wood spoke) that the American had tampered with the apparatus so there was no result. In fact, the result had been conclusive. Wood thanked his hosts and returned to his hotel to write an article for the magazine *Nature*, definitively debunking N-rays.

How had the French establishment been taken in? First, there was a great degree of wishful thinking in the experiments. All measurements had to be done by eye, noting tiny changes in relative illumination in darkened rooms. It was easy to see things that weren't there and even easier when you wanted them to be there. France was still smarting from her defeat in the Franco-Prussian War of 1870. Added injury came in the shape of Röntgen's discovery of X-rays and the associated renaissance in German science. It was an era of great discoveries and France needed one to call its own. On this occasion the French chose what they wanted to see, not what was there.

It is perhaps ironic that the Leconte prize had not originally been intended for Blondlot but for a Frenchman who really would change the face of science – Pierre Curie.

❧

Of course one of the best ways to keep your dubious discovery from being exposed is to keep it secret. Sometimes for ever.

❧

The secret electuary

Patent law allows for new inventions and processes to be described without that publication opening up the inventor to copycats but the variable enforcement of patent law in earlier days led many to choose the easier but more problematic course of total secrecy (see page 171).

One such man was William Cockburn. Cockburn was not a quack; indeed, he was educated in medicine at one of Britain's finest medical schools in Edinburgh and held a respected position in the navy. As Physician to the Blue (the Blue being one of the three squadrons of the British Navy – the Red, the White and the Blue), he was charged with ensuring the health of men aboard ship, no mean feat in an age of poor sanitation, abysmal nutrition and tropical diseases.

The one that particularly bothered the navy was the flux, or dysentery as we would call it, and this, rather unpleasantly, was the subject of conversation aboard Captain Meese's ship *Sandwich*, one July evening in 1696 as it lay at anchor in Torbay. Around the table with Meese and Cockburn were another captain, Beaumont, and the admiral, the Earl Berkeley of Stratton. Having complimented Cockburn on his medical powers, the naval men commented that what was most wanting in the modern navy was a cure for the flux. No one of course expected an immediate answer so the entire company was taken aback when Cockburn announced that he had just the thing and would happily test it out the following day.

Next morning, around a hundred sailors with the flux (they were very easy to find) were presented aboard the *Sandwich* for treatment, twenty of whom were so ill that they couldn't leave their hammocks. Each man was given a mild purge and then a dose of Cockburn's medicine, a secret powder, which was repeated regularly for three days. And it worked. Or so Cockburn claimed.

After just ten days even the weakest of the men could stand. The navy was delighted. Sir Cloudesley Shovell – the Admiral of the Blue, who in 1707 would drown along with 700 men in a great disaster off the Isles of Scilly – ordered a large batch for his expeditions to the Mediterranean. Here he reported it a great success. More and more was ordered. Cockburn began to build up a substantial private practice based on his naval reputation.

For every other doctor in England the question was: what was actually in Cockburn's medicine and did it really work? The answer to the first question was that Cockburn wasn't going to tell you. As he put it himself: 'I conceal this medicine, because I think it better than the Fr. Ipicochoana [ipecacuana, a purgative] itself, by which Helvetius has made so plentiful a fortune.'

In other words, it was too valuable a secret to give away. As to its efficacy, Cockburn himself tells us that a 'scandalous' experiment was done by other doctors, which seemed to cast doubt on the cure; but fortunately his old dining chum, Lord Berkeley, had just been promoted to lead the Commissioners of the Navy. He overruled the study and ordered the purchase of further supplies.

In 1700 the navy made one last attempt to get the College of Physicians 'on board' by asking them to comment on Cockburn's plans for naval surgeons to record all symptoms of disease on schematic charts, along with the results of applying his medicines. It was, for its era, as good an attempt at a drug trial as was known, but the College of Physicians were dismissive, claiming the method was 'neither authentick enough to engage our Belief, nor Consistent with those made by other Physicians in the same Countries'. Privately they were less reserved, referring to Cockburn simply as 'an old very rich quack'.

So the question as to what was in Cockburn's potion and whether it worked remains unanswered to this day. Certainly the College didn't believe a word of it, whilst a desperate Admiralty put their faith in every word. Repeated sea trials would suggest that at least some of those with the flux recovered under Cockburn's treatment. Had the College of Physicians not scotched the plan, his request for details of symptoms, and the effects of his treatments on them, to be minutely recorded in situ, might have answered the question once and for all.

Despite the sniping, Cockburn had the last laugh. Having made his powder into an electuary (a sweetened medicinal paste) suitable for the general public, and with the continued backing of the navy, he did indeed die 'very rich', whether or not his electuary was a piece of quackery. He was buried in the centre aisle of Westminster Abbey, and his secret with him.

❦

Perhaps saddest amongst the travelling
hucksters and bogus patent-medicine sellers
are those who accidentally make a great
observation, only to have scorn poured on it due
to the 'less reliable' aspects of their work.

❦

The honest fraudster

If Gustavus Katterfelto had a disadvantage in life, it was that he was a quack, and a well-known one at that. Not that many physicians in the eighteenth century had a much better record than him but his chosen method of promoting himself, through self-laudatory advertising and expansive public shows, had him marked down by those in authority as an undoubted charlatan. Or, in his view, as a 'Moral and Divine Philosopher, Teacher in Mathematics and Natural Philosophy'.

Since the late 1770s, Katterfelto, who was probably Prussian by birth, had been travelling England as a touring lecturer, a strange halfway house between respectable gentleman scientist and huckster. Unlike the patent-medicine fraudsters of the early USA, he did not salt his audience with stooges ready to be cured by his magical panacea but instead gave the paying public a rather good show of the 'wonders of modern science'.

His equipment included the latest globes and orreries, a telescope, an air pump, a hydrogen balloon, electrical generators and a projecting microscope that allowed his paying public to see the marvels of the invisibly small world. He also enrolled his family in the demonstrations, in one instance strapping a metal helmet to his daughter's head and then lifting her up by it using a magnet. None of this particularly marked him out from the many respectable scientists of the era who performed public demonstrations with much the same apparatus.

However, to be fair, Katterfelto did go a bit further than this. As a lover of the mysterious and the occult, he didn't like to spoil the sense of admiration that his demonstrations evoked with prosaic scientific explanations. Indeed, he actively promoted the idea that there was something spooky in his act by working only in the presence of his 'magical' black cat, whose offspring he would offer for sale after the show. Following the main performance, he could also quite easily be induced, for a suitable fee, to give further instruction – to those with the money to hear it – on his infallible methods for winning at dice, cards and billiards.

And to be absolutely honest, he did have a patent medicine for sale, which he called 'Dr Bato's Remedy' and which would mark both the highest and the lowest points of his achievement.

In London in 1782, there was a sudden and virulent outbreak of influenza. In days long before anti-viral drugs, this cut a swathe through the population, provoking widespread panic and leaving doctors at a loss. In fact no one had any real idea what caused this (or any other) disease, or how it was spread, although it was still widely held that an unfavourable alignment of planets led to influenza.

One doctor, however, did have the answer – 'Doctor' Katterfelto. Having taken public rooms in Piccadilly, he issued a series of press advertisements, headed 'Wonders', after which he added the words, 'Wonders, Wonders, Wonders!' in case you hadn't got the gist of it the first time. These claimed that he was able to demonstrate both the cause and the cure of the influenza epidemic. People who handed over their money (three shillings for a front row seat, one shilling at the back) were treated to a three-hour show that included a demonstration of Katterfelto's 'solar microscope', which projected a magnified image from a microscope on to the wall. Under this device

Katterfelto would place a tiny drop, 'no bigger than a pinhead', of ordinary water.

To their horror the audience saw that the drop contained millions of tiny creatures or 'insects' as he called them, all writhing around. The experiment was repeated with drops of blood, beer, vinegar and milk, and with pieces of bread and cheese, all of which were alive with microscopic creatures. This, he grandly announced, was the cause of the flu – a host of invisible insects. Furthermore he also had a cure, which was, of course, Dr Bato's Remedy – only five shillings a bottle.

This performance may have delighted the public – it impressed even George III – but it turned the medical establishment firmly against Katterfelto. Denounced as a fraud and a quack, he was satirised in plays and poems, and described by William Cowper, no less, as:

> *Katterfelto, with his hair on end*
> *At his own wonders, wondering for his bread.*

In the face of a hostile medical establishment, and with Dr Bato's Remedy not having had the miraculous effects he had hoped for it, his fame soon faded. By the end of 1783, Katterfelto was advertising his equipment for sale and setting off once again on the road as an itinerant performer. Despite being portrayed in cartoons with bulging bags of money, he actually made precious little for his efforts and spent the rest of his life scraping a living for his family whilst not always successfully avoiding being gaoled as a vagrant.

And the most galling part was that he was almost right. Whilst his patent medicine was certainly useless, his observation was brilliant. As soon as he had invented the microscope, Anton van Leeuwenhoek had noticed the same tiny creatures that Katterfelto had seen, but it was the Prussian showman who first associated them with disease.

Although it is true that his 'insects' were bacteria, not the virus that actually causes flu, the idea that tiny active particles could create disease was not only correct but far ahead of its time. It would be another eighty years before Louis Pasteur (see page 106) would experimentally prove the connection between bacteria and disease, taking a richly deserved fame for one of the greatest breakthroughs in medical science. Gustavus Katterfelto, meanwhile, died in anonymous poverty in 1799.

⤬

Many a scientist may have no
interest in outright fraud but simply fancies a
bit of a practical joke. When it comes to great
discoveries, however, a joker needs to tread
carefully as who knows where their
prank will lead?

⤬

The lying stones

One of the great dangers of science is discovering the thing you've always hoped to find. Have you really found it? Or have you manipulated your findings to get the result you wanted? Of course, it doesn't help when your colleagues have deliberately set you up.

That was the lamentable fate of Johann Beringer, born in 1667, a medical professor at the University of Würzburg, now known only for the unfortunate incident of the *Lügensteine* or lying stones.

Johann Beringer was not popular. His colleagues in the university once claimed that he 'was so arrogant and despised them all', which is not a good sign. Perhaps it should have made him a little more careful when his researches took a strange turn.

Beringer was keen on collecting fossils, which he would search out on the nearby Mount Eivelstadt. When his work kept him from this, he would pay local boys to scour the slopes and bring him back anything interesting. And on 31 May 1725, interesting things certainly began arriving. The first three 'finds' brought to him by three local boys were small pieces of limestone, two apparently carved into the shape of worms and a third that looked like a stylised representation of the sun. At the time, the process by which fossils were created – indeed, the very nature of fossils themselves – was unknown, so these highly unusual objects didn't rouse Beringer's suspicions.

He became more intrigued as the stream of objects began to turn into a flood. In just six months, nearly 2,000 stones were brought to him. Many were carved with animals, but shown 'in the flesh' rather than in the skeletised form more usual for fossils. Amongst the lizards, frogs, slugs, plants and insects, there were also still more unusual items. Some stones revealed what appeared to be astronomical objects – a comet and planets. Others had words on them, in a selection of languages including Babylonian, Latin and Syriac, as well as a most impressive group inscribed in Hebrew with the name for God: YHWH – Jehovah.

The question was: what had created these stones? Beringer puzzled over the matter for months as he prepared to publish his great work on the subject, *Lithographiae Wirceburgensis*. In its pages he hypothesised that the stones might have been created by 'the marvellous force of petrifying nature', or perhaps they were the creation of ancient heathen Germans, a notion that he dismissed as he didn't think the heathen ancient Germans went around writing down the Hebrew word for God. In the end he concluded that at least some of the stones had been created by God, for fun, and had been hidden in the hills by Him, perhaps to test mankind's faith.

There was of course another possibility, one nagging thought, that Beringer felt he had to address. Could the stones be fakes? Certainly others thought they might be, as he recorded:

> I caught the rumour circulating throughout the city, especially among prominent and learned men, that every one of these stones, which, on the advice of wise men, I proposed to expound in a published treatise, were 'recently sculpted by hand, made to look as though at different periods they had been resurrected from a very old burial, and sold to me as to one indifferent to fraud and caught up in the blind greed of curiosity . . .'

The rumour was in fact being circulated by two of his colleagues, J. Ignatz Roderick, Professor of Geography, Algebra and Analysis, and Johann Georg von Eckhart, Privy Councillor and Librarian to the Court and University. They had put the word out because they were wondering whether their little joke had perhaps gone too far and they were keen for Beringer to pull back from publishing a book that would make him a laughing stock.

Beringer, however, was adamant. The stones could not be fakes. Certainly some were a little crude and showed what looked like the tell-tale signs of having been roughly carved with a pocket knife, but why would anyone go to the trouble of faking them? And how could any faker create 2,000 of them in so short a time? The very idea was out of the question. The stones were indubitably a product of nature.

Roderick and von Eckhart tried one last gambit. Going to the place where they knew Beringer had recently been searching for (and finding) the stones, they placed one last clue. The final stone had an inscription on it, which read: VIVAT BERENGARIUS – GOTT.'

By now it was too late. The book was published, just as

Beringer discovered the message wishing him long life, apparently written by God. Mortified, the duped professor immediately brought a legal case against Roderick and von Eckhart, which Beringer won. Roderick was forced to leave Würzburg in disgrace, while von Eckhart lost his job and his university privileges.

Nevertheless, no legal case could restore Beringer's credibility and his name rapidly became a byword for arrogant credulity. In a desperate attempt to limit the damage, he tried to buy up every copy of *Lithographiae Wirceburgensis*, but this only made the surviving copies more prized. So collectable did the book become that in 1767, twenty-seven years after his death, it was republished in all its credulous glory, complete with the twenty-one plates of lying stones.

∽

Being a bit dishonest does not preclude
anyone from being a perfectly good scientist.
Sometimes a bit of ethical equivocation can be
just what the doctor ordered.

∽

Hunter's giant

John Hunter, born in 1728, was not the sort of medical man to try out his ideas on other people (see page 301). In his attempts to discover whether the venereal disease gonorrhoea developed with time into syphilis, he was reported to have injected his own foreskin with the pus from the urethra of a gonorrhoea victim. Sadly, the patient he chose as a subject also had syphilis, so Hunter concluded that what we now know are two distinct diseases were in fact aspects of the same one, putting the study of venereal disease back by decades. It was nevertheless a noble example of his own favourite dictum: 'Don't think, try it.'

He put this dictum to use in other areas of his varied life. Hunter was responsible for coining the terms for teeth, such as molars and incisors; he was the first doctor to perform an artificial insemination; and he was perhaps the first doctor ever to prescribe a placebo to test whether a drug actually worked. His first student was the celebrated Edward Jenner and he was a friend of Benjamin Franklin, Lord Byron (see page 312) and Casanova, which must have made for some interesting dinner parties. He also suggested that fossils must be at least thousands of years old, a century before anyone dared float the idea publicly.

At his large house on Leicester Square in London, he kept a collection of over 14,000 anatomical specimens, as well as a museum of stuffed animals including many exotic creatures, as he had first refusal on any dying animal in the king's menagerie. There was one other thing that he really wanted for his collection, however, and it would prove an area where his ethics were not quite as pure.

Charles Byrne had been born in Ireland in 1761 but reached the apogee of his fame on the stage of the Haymarket theatre in London in 1782. What made him so noteworthy was not his performance but his size. He was the star of the show *The Giant's Causeway*, which was appropriate as he was indeed a giant, standing around 8 feet 4 inches tall. Whilst many had an interest in this living Goliath, John Hunter and some of his fellow collectors had a more morbid motivation. He would, they agreed, make a fine specimen for their collections – but only when dead.

Tragically for Byrne, their chance to make their macabre dreams come true arrived only a year later when he died, on 1 June 1783, at his lodgings in Charing Cross. If Byrne's death was sudden – he was just twenty-two – he had still had time to plan for it. He was perfectly well aware that anatomising and displaying unusual human bodies was very fashionable amongst London's anatomists and that men like Hunter often paid body-snatchers to dig up interesting specimens. Byrne might have been an alcoholic but he was not without means and he determined to foil his would-be collectors. Converting all his wealth into a single banknote of £700, he left orders to his executors that he was to be buried at sea, far from the reach of the 'resurrectionists'.

It is unclear what happened next but shortly after his death the banknote disappeared, perhaps leaving the undertaker more open to other 'suggestions' for what might be done with the corpse. In the end, that suggestion was an offer no working man could refuse. John Hunter paid £500 to have the giant's remains removed from the coffin and replaced with rocks, which were buried at sea in its stead. Charles Byrne's body was dissected and his skeleton removed and preserved. It is still in the collection that bears Hunter's name at the Royal College of Surgeons in London.

∽

Some scientists might have had reasons
for their little 'lapses' of honesty, but some of
the less scrupulous will say almost anything
to get their own way.

Schrödinger's request

In the world of science, and even more so in the rarefied field of quantum physics, it's easy to forget that the practitioners of these often arcane arts are themselves, well, human. And few have been more 'human' than Erwin Schrödinger.

Schrödinger had rocketed to fame (at least in the world of physics) in 1926 with the publication of four papers that revolutionised quantum mechanics. Just a year later he succeeded to the most revered position in the field as successor to the great Max Planck at the Friedrich Wilhelm University in Berlin.

These were difficult times in Germany. By 1933 the rise of the Nazis was leading many German scientists, particularly those from a Jewish background, to consider leaving the country. This, in turn, led to an unusual 'shopping spree' by senior staff at universities in Britain and the USA, keen to entice the finest German scientific minds to their institutions. This was what brought Frederick Lindemann (see page 305), head of physics at Oxford University, to Berlin in that year.

Amongst the scientists that Lindemann was interested in was Fritz London, one of the young Jewish assistants working for Schrödinger. The two professors agreed to meet to discuss the possibility. What happened next surprised Lindemann as, when he told the great professor that his assistant had asked for time to think over the idea, Schrödinger had replied: 'Offer it to me; if he does not go, I'll take the position.'

This was an offer that really couldn't be refused. Schrödinger was one of the very brightest stars in the physics firmament; he wanted to come to England; and he wasn't even Jewish. Lindemann rushed home to make arrangements.

Thanks to funding from ICI and the offer of a fellowship at the very convivial Magdalen College, Oxford, the deal was arranged, but then a small problem arose. Schrödinger wrote, demanding that if he were to come, Artur March, an associate professor at Innsbruck University in Austria, had to come with him. This was a shade puzzling. March wasn't Jewish either and there was no evidence that Schrödinger had ever previously been so keen on the two working together. Frantic arrangements were made, however, and in November 1933, Erwin Schrödinger and his family, together with Artur March and his family, arrived at their impressive new lodgings in Oxford.

It was only now that the famously prudish Lindemann found out the real reasons behind the move. Schrödinger was not particularly interested in Oxford and hated the all-male, high-table world of Magdalen. What he did greatly enjoy, however, was Artur March's wife, Hilde. Indeed, the serially unfaithful Schrödinger had been pursuing Hilde for some time and the two families' leisurely trip to England, via the Austrian Tyrol, had given him the opportunity to consummate their love. By the time they all arrived in Oxford, Hilde was pregnant with Schrödinger's child. To make matters worse, in Lindemann's eyes at least, they appeared to have no intention of keeping this secret but wanted to live in an open *ménage à trois*.

Fortunately for Schrödinger, the potential scandal was entirely overwhelmed by the news that he had won the Nobel prize, something that could encourage any university to 'look the other way'. Fortunately for Lindemann, Schrödinger didn't intend staying long at Oxford anyway. He briefly considered a post at Princeton, where Einstein was working, but considered the salary offered to be 'not sufficiently agreeable', even though it would have made him the second-highest-paid physicist on earth. Princeton too got wind of his desire to live in a *ménage à trois* with his wife and lover and became cooler in their approach. In response, Schrödinger referred to Princeton as 'a quaint ceremonious village of puny demi-gods on stilts'. Needless to say, the appointment was never made.

Having also entertained the idea of a professorship in Edinburgh, Schrödinger finally returned to his native Austria in 1936 to take up the chair in physics at the University of Graz. Here some of his chickens finally came home to roost. Hitler had not been best pleased with Schrödinger's exit from Berlin and, when the Anschluss with Austria occurred in March 1938, Schrödinger feared he might lose his post. In undoubtedly the most shameful act of his career, he wrote an open, grovelling letter to Hitler, praising the Nazi state and looking forward to serving 'my homeland'. It didn't work and Schrödinger was sacked for 'political unreliability'.

Schrödinger managed to escape once more, returning briefly to Oxford where any disapproval for his personal life had been far eclipsed by the public reaction to his 'pro-Nazi' letter. Initially many had believed that the letter had been written under extreme duress but when it turned out he had, without prompting, penned the letter whilst on a convivial skiing trip, his colleagues' attitude quickly changed.

Lindemann commented, 'Is he mad? Doesn't he realise after this letter he has published what people think of him?' An astonishingly unrepentant Schrödinger replied: 'What I have written, I have written. Nobody forced me to do anything. This is supposed to be a land of freedom and what I do is nobody's concern.'

Erwin Schrödinger finally found the sort of life he had been looking for in Eire, where Prime Minister Eamon de Valera, himself a former mathematician, had set up an Institute for Advanced Study. Here Schrödinger stayed for eighteen years, living openly with his wife and a new Irish mistress.

$\sim$

And finally some things, regardless of the intent of the perpetrator, are just simply, magnificently wrong.

$\sim$

American pi

Possibly the most famous thing about the number pi, other than the fact that it describes the ratio of a circle's circumference to its diameter, is that it is 'irrational' – in other words, it cannot be expressed as a fraction and has an infinite number of digits. Unless you live in Indiana.

This was the home of country doctor and supremely confident amateur mathematician Dr Edward Johnston Goodwin. Here, in the town of Solitude, during the first week of March 1888, he came upon a wholly different and novel value for pi when, in his own words: 'the author was supernaturally taught the exact measure of the circle . . . and no authority in the science of numbers can tell how the ratio was discovered.'

This, of itself, is not all that unusual as pi has for centuries exerted a strange hold over eccentrics. Many have felt that its irrationality was, well, not only irrational but, frankly, untidy. What made Goodwin different was that he applied to patent his new value for pi in the USA, England, France, Germany, Belgium, Austria and Spain. As far as the patent offices were concerned, what mattered was that the work was novel, which it certainly was, rather then whether it was mathematically correct. The patents were granted.

The emboldened Dr Goodwin, feeling that the patent examiners of the world were behind him, decided to present his new pi as an exhibit at the 1893 Columbian Exposition in Chicago and was granted a stand. When the organisers learnt of the exact nature of his 'educational show', they withdrew their permission while offering the suggestion that he might prefer to publish his work in a mathematical journal.

This should have been the end of Goodwin's pi but, thanks to the *American Mathematical Monthly*, it was not. This magazine was then in its first year and, being short on material and money, was known to publish some 'less rigorous' work, provided the fees were paid and a few caveats were placed in the article. Goodwin's proof of his new value of pi appeared under the title 'Quadrature of the Circle' in the Queries and Information section of issue seven, volume one, preceded by the editorial note: 'Published at the request of the author.' The work is unusual in the extreme, using various mathematical techniques to derive not one but nine values for pi, ranging from 2.56 to 4 from which Goodwin, for no clear reason, plumps for 3.2 – the number he patented.

Now, surely, Goodwin's pi was cooked? But no. With the weight behind him of the patent office and publication in a learned journal, he managed to persuade his local representative in the Indiana House of Representatives to introduce a House Bill (no. 246), requiring that, in Indiana at least, pi should be 3.2. In return he offered to provide the patented number free to schools and the legislature in the state (the bill required everyone else to pay to use it).

Goodwin undoubtedly had a patent, and pi was quite a useful number so, just in case, the bill was drawn up. Not everyone in Indianapolis took this seriously, however, and the bill was play-fully sent to the Committee on Canals where, a local paper noted, 'midst general cheerfulness . . . , in the swamps, the bill would find a deserved grave.'

However, no one seems to have told the Canals Committee about the joke. Mathematics not really being their field, they floated the bill back to the Education Committee. Proving surprisingly short on education themselves, they returned the bill to the House with a recommendation that it pass. Astonishingly, the House then allowed a second and a third reading. To top this, they passed it with 67 votes to none, and forwarded it on to the Senate. Perhaps some still considered this a joke, as the bill was handed to the Temperance Committee, perhaps on the assumption that everyone who had previously agreed it must have been drunk. Perhaps the Senate were too, as they returned it with a recommendation that it pass.

By now the bill was in newspapers across the country, and much general merriment ensued everywhere, except in Indianapolis. Whilst the Senate joked about the bill, all the politicians conceded that they knew too little mathematics to discount it, particularly when it came from work published in a learned journal and subject to many patents.

Fortunately, at this moment the bill came to the attention of C.A. Waldo, Professor of Mathematics at Purdue University, who just happened to be in the Indianapolis Senate on the day that it was considering changing one of the fundamental constants of his subject. After hurried exchanges with senators, he arranged to brief them privately on the lunacy of the proposed bill. That evening when they reconvened, the bill did not pass. However, lest anyone forget how close Indiana came to changing the laws of mathematics, the bill was not thrown right out, but simply postponed indefinitely, or *sine die*, as legislators like to put it, so it still lurks in the Senate's papers to this day.

10

To Boldly Go . . .

(In which we take a final look at some of those
brave souls who have ventured into the
darkness in the name of science without being
scared. Or at least not admitting it.)

Science – the Endless Frontier.

> Vannevar Bush, *A Report to the President* (1945)

Science – the Endless Expenditure.

> Vannevar Bush, quoted in Thomas Hager, *Force of
> Nature: The Life of Linus Pauling* (1995)

If science is an adventure, it certainly has an uncertain destination, as I hope these tales from some of the more adventurous scientists – both mentally and physically – show. But we should start at the beginning with a piece of mental gymnastics so brilliant that it inspired one of the most famous stories in the whole of science.

✑

Eureka!

Perhaps the most famous word in science, indeed the epitome of that marvellous moment of scientific revelation, was almost certainly never spoken in the context often claimed. This has often taken the shine off the reputation of Archimedes (see page 234), one of the greatest mathematicians and engineers of the ancient world, which is a shame as, whilst he may never have run naked down the street shouting 'Eureka!' the rest of the account is probably true.

The story goes that King Hiero II – a low-born commander in the wars against Carthage who had managed to seize power in Syracuse around 270 BC – invited Archimedes to the palace to present a problem to him.

The monarch had ordered a precious votive crown for a temple in the city as thanks for his victories in war. He had chosen the maker and sent from the treasury a large quantity of gold with which to manufacture it. In time the beautifully wrought crown had been returned to him and he had dedicated it in the temple. Now a rumour had come to his ears that the maker, for all his craft, was a cheat and had kept some of the gold for himself, which vexed Hiero mightily.

Of course the first thing palace officials would have done on receiving the crown was to weigh it to confirm that it weighed the same as the quantity of gold that the maker had been given. When they did so, the weight was indeed correct, but the rumour suggested that the goldsmith had tricked the king, alloying the gold with extra, cheaper silver, something not only offensive to Hiero but in his mind highly offensive to the gods to whom the crown had been dedicated. So he summoned Archimedes to discover a solution. In the process of doing so, he invented the whole field of hydrostatics.

We may never know exactly what provided the inspiration for the solution but the famous bath story was already current in the first century BC, during the lifetime of the Roman architect Marcus Vitruvius Pollio (known better as just Vitruvius), who recounts it in Book IX, Chapter 10 of his *De Architectura*. He tells us:

> he by chance went to a bath, and being in the vessel, perceived that, as his body became immersed, the water ran out of the vessel. Whence, catching at the method to be adopted for the solution of the proposition, he immediately followed it up, leapt out of the vessel in joy, and, returning home naked, cried out with a loud voice that he had found that of which he was in search, for he continued exclaiming, in Greek, Eureka! (I have found it out).

This suggests that, when bathing, Archimedes had realised that the volume of water displaced by the immersion of his own body was equal to the volume of his body.

To solve the mystery of the gold, he filled a bowl to the brim, placed in it a piece of gold that weighed the same as the crown, and noted down how much water spilt over the brim. He then repeated the experiment with a piece of silver of the same weight.

This time it displaced more water than had the gold. Gold is far denser and so a piece of any given weight has a much smaller volume than that of silver.

Finally he filled the pot once again to the brim and then placed in it the crown itself. This displaced a quantity of water somewhere between the volumes displaced by the lumps of gold and silver. The result suggested that the crown contained some gold but was not pure. From this Archimedes could work out exactly how much silver the craftsman had surreptitiously alloyed with the gold as a ratio of the displaced volumes of water. It was a brilliant experiment, using just water and logic to untangle the proportions of two metals bound tightly together in alloy. Hiero was rightly impressed. Although we never hear of him again, the craftsman, we might imagine, having been caught out, was less so.

Whilst the golden crown story may well be true, the bath and the running around naked shouting 'Eureka' bit – usually everyone's favourite part of the story – is almost certainly not. In fact, we know from Plutarch's *Parallel Lives – Life of Marcellus*, Chapter 17, that Archimedes didn't really like taking baths anyway:

> Oftimes Archimedes' servants got him against his will to the baths, to wash and anoint him, and yet being there, he would ever be drawing out of the geometrical figures, even in the very embers of the chimney. And while they were anointing of him with oils and sweet savours, with his fingers he drew lines upon his naked body, so far was he taken from himself, and brought into ecstasy or trance, with the delight he had in the study of geometry.

This glimpse of a disconnected genius – churlish and difficult with his servants, reluctant to engage in the everyday world and even more reluctant to bathe, yet retaining an almost childlike delight in the purity of geometry and mathematics, the perfection of shapes and form – is perhaps a truer view of the man. Had he enjoyed bathing more, he might have made his great discovery earlier. But then if he had enjoyed bathing more, he wouldn't have been Archimedes.

⁓

The scientist who 'boldly goes' is not necessarily heading out into a physical wilderness. Some of the bravest are simply setting out to explore places other folk dare not look.

⁓

Incisions, incisions . . .

Sometimes the laws and customs of a time are not conducive to the development of a scientific discipline. Never has this been more the case than in the field of surgery. People are peculiarly protective about their bodies and many cultures have gone to great lengths to ensure that others don't get to fiddle around inside them – even after they're dead. This has, of course, rather hindered those trying to find out what makes us tick and how it can be mended. This was the dilemma facing one of the greatest surgical minds of all time in the middle of the second century AD.

Galen was born in Pergamum in what is today Turkey around AD 129. Galen's father, Nicon, had been a successful and affluent architect, and he had given his son a broad classical education in mathematics, logic, grammar and philosophy. However, it was to medicine that young Galen turned when he was just sixteen. According to legend, his father had a dream revealing his son's destiny in the subject. Whilst this would probably be

enough to make most independently-minded teenagers immediately enrol in the next travelling circus, Galen took his father's
advice.

The difficulties facing a trainee doctor in the Roman world
were substantial. First, one had to choose which sort of doctor
to become. Physicians for the wealthy treated their patients in
accordance with theoretical principles and were known as
Dogmatists. Physicians for slaves relied upon trial and error,
and were known as Empiricists. Between these two extremes
were the Methodists, whose sole concern was not hymn singing
but disease itself, ignoring the patient and his or her medical
history. Galen recognised that it was necessary to develop
theories from practical observation and experience, as well as
to test existing theory against observations, modifying or aban-
doning it if it seemed not to 'work'.

Galen's major problem was getting his hands on a body to
experiment on. Infuriatingly, human dissection was banned
everywhere in the Roman world – well, everywhere but Egypt.
So, in AD 152 he moved to Alexandria where, thanks to the
country's long history of embalming, human dissection was still
permitted. His time in Alexandria gave Galen a passion for
anatomy, which would be both the making of and, many
centuries later, the breaking of his reputation. By opening up
human bodies, both living and dead, he was able to view the
body as a machine and to brilliantly deduce many of its functions.
In his later career he would repeat his investigations on animals
in front of astounded crowds.

One favourite, if slightly gothic, demonstration involved cutting
an incision down the back of a live pig, severing groups of spinal
nerves to show their function. Of course all the while the pig
would squeal until he tied off the laryngeal nerve when the
pig suddenly stopped. And so he proceeded, removing or tying
off various vital pathways and identifying their purpose from the
effect. He tied off animals' ureters to demonstrate kidney and

bladder function, and closed off veins and arteries to prove that, contrary to the popular theory of the day, they carried blood and not air.

After finishing his training, Galen returned to his native Pergamum where again he came up against the ban on dissection. Now, however, he found a novel way around this, all thanks to one of the more gruesome entertainments of the Roman world.

Gladiators were the football superstars of their day, the subject of adulatory graffiti on public baths and the pin-ups of young girls everywhere. A good gladiator, although a slave, was worth a fortune to his owner and the very best doctors were hired to tend to them. For Galen this was the perfect opportunity. Gladiators often suffered horrific injuries – indeed, they were almost 'self-dissecting' – and in repairing these Galen could not only make a good living but get a chance to explore inside the living flesh of the machine. Provided it was a gladiator that made the incision in the arena and not a doctor on the operating table, no one complained if he then used these wounds – or 'windows on to anatomy' as he called them – to explore the inner workings of the body.

At the same time Galen also pioneered the treatment of the more usual sports injuries – sprains, breaks, dislocations and concussions. From these he developed 130 of the 150 basic surgical techniques that are still in use today – everything from brain surgery to repairing compressed fractures, to the use of traction beds to straighten broken limbs. Even at the end of a gladiator's career there was one last procedure that Galen developed that would assist his patient in his new life as a free man: the removal of the tattoo that marked him as a slave.

Galen's fame spread and soon the capital, Rome, beckoned. Here he took every opportunity to put his rivals in the shade. One such occasion was provided by the arrival of a Persian merchant, complaining of a loss of feeling in the ring and little fingers and half the middle finger of one hand. For some time Roman doctors had been applying unguents and creams to the fingers in the hope of stimulating them but to no effect.

Galen asked him an unusual question: had he hurt his arm recently? The question must have been quite surprising to the Roman, as the problem was clearly in his fingers. But Galen was right. The man said he had taken a bad fall and hurt his back. Galen diagnosed a spinal lesion and recommended bed rest and soothing compresses for the injury site. It worked and the man's fingers recovered.

Rome was good to Galen. He lived to be eighty-seven but, in the centuries that followed, in which Galen became a revered authority on anatomy, the city's laws would also lead to the eventual loss of his standing. Although here he could serve emperors and make a fortune, he was no longer working with gladiators and he was forbidden human dissection. Instead, he relied on animal dissection, apparently unaware of the huge differences between the anatomy of humans and the creatures he was studying.

When, in 1543, the Flemish anatomist Andreas Vesalius – who by then had free access to human cadavers – compared what he saw in the anatomy theatre with what was written in Galen, he realised that much of it was simply wrong. The inside of a dog, or even the inside of his preferred Barbary apes, was not the same as the inside of a human. Galen's teaching was abandoned and even his most insightful works lay unread. Galen's work, both good and bad, was set aside and much of the knowledge gleaned by the first man to treat the body as a machine was forgotten.

❦

Every invention and every discovery has its moment. An observation at the wrong time or a suggestion in an era that doesn't want to hear it can turn huge potential breakthroughs into no more than missed opportunities. This is a risk that every scientist takes but few misses were greater than Hero's.

❦

Hero's engine

Like so many scientific heroes, Hero of Alexandria (see page 13) has every right to be a lot more famous than he actually is. Working in the first century AD, he was, even then, an unusual character. Not your average classical scholar but, as the later mathematician Pappus puts it, one of the 'wonder workers', Hero was a designer of automatically-operating mechanical toys, with which he amused and bemused the people of the city. The machines that he built used gravity, pressure, heat and water to power devices that appeared to operate without human intervention and would have surprised and bewildered an eighteenth-century European as much as they did Romans and Alexandrians.

Tucked away in his surviving notes lies something far more extraordinary – his plans for an aeliopile. He describes this 'novelty toy' as two copper tubes soldered to the top of a sealed metal container. These passed through two metal sleeves feeding into each side of a copper sphere that could rotate between them. From the sphere emerged two nozzles facing opposite each other. When water was boiled in the lower sealed compartment, he described how steam would rise through the tubes and into the ball before shooting out of the nozzles, making the ball spin round to the delight of his audience. And they should have been delighted and amazed. Spinning at around 1,500 rpm, this was the fastest man-made rotating object in the ancient world.

More than that, it was the first ever use of jet power. And, more amazing still, it was, of course, a prototype steam engine. Had Hero combined this 'toy' with the piston – something that his fellow Alexandrian, the barber Ctesibius, had invented some 300 or so years earlier – he could have created a working steam engine. But he didn't.

To Hero the steam engine – the workhorse that created the modern world – was simply a curiosity. There were fundamental problems with his design that certainly didn't help. The main snag with it was its efficiency – or lack of it. To allow the ball to spin freely, the joints had to be made quite loose, but if the joints were loose, a lot of the steam escaped through them. Then there was the issue of fuel. In the Roman world the boiler would have to have been powered by wood, which would have to be collected by someone – probably a slave. So if the useful energy gained from burning the wood to make the steam to turn the ball was less than the energy used by the slave to collect the wood, the device would be making a loss and the slave might as well be told to do the work himself.

Hero's steam engine had even bigger drawbacks. Those very slaves who would be needed to collect the fuel were themselves an obstacle to there even being a Roman industrial revolution. The main use of steam engines during our own Industrial Revolution was for producing cheap and readily available power. Hiring people in the eighteenth century to do jobs by hand was expensive and it was difficult to always get skilled people when you needed them. Steam engines, however, could work day and night without rest, they were always available and they were very strong.

It was different for the Romans. They already had a source of cheap and plentiful labour in the form of slaves. Whilst the slaves themselves may have liked the idea of machines to do their work for them, the slave-owner saw no need for mechanical help. There was also the question of what would happen if machines did replace slaves – where would the slaves go, what would they do? No one wanted another Spartacus.

And so Hero's greatest invention was condemned to be no more than a party novelty, merely another description of a marvellous mechanical engine in a book in the vast Alexandrian library. The Industrial Revolution would have to wait.

∽

Science and religion have not always been happy bedfellows, particularly when the observations of the former clash with the beliefs of the latter. Challenging dogma with scientific fact is a dangerous game that requires another form of bravery.

∽

The sun in splendour

Although Nicolaus Copernicus had published his *De revolutionibus orbium coelestium* in 1543, postulating that the sun and not the earth lay at the centre of the solar system, sixty years later the idea was still not popular.

The earlier system, developed by Claudius Ptolemy in Alexandria in the early second century AD, rather comfortingly placed the earth at the centre and invoked the planets in a series of twirling epicycles to explain why, if this was the case, the planets didn't move in a straight line across the night sky. This was the system that the mediaeval Church had adopted, mirroring as it does the Biblical view that God had placed mankind at the centre of his creation. It was also the system that an awful lot of people and the Church continued to like.

Galileo Galilei wasn't one of them and he was armed with something to disprove it. Whilst it is still a matter of conjecture who built the first telescope, in 1609 it came to the attention of Galileo, then a professor of mathematics at the University of Padua, that an optical device existed for making distant objects appear nearer. Being a practical man, he built one for himself, with a lead tube and some spectacle lenses. Regardless of who first thought up the instrument, it was Galileo who decided to point it at the night sky. What he saw there amazed him and would change our view of the universe. Today he is remembered for having discovered the four moons around Jupiter and for first seeing craters and mountains on the moon, but it was his view of another planet that would really change everything.

Galileo was a Copernican, but he needed proof that the earth revolved around the sun and not the other way round. This was an era when holding views contrary to those of the Church, even on matters of science, could land you in hot water – sometimes literally – so he had to be careful. However, what he saw when he first pointed his telescope at Venus in October 1610 was so revealing that he would risk his own life to publicise it.

Venus, when seen through a telescope, exhibited all the phases, from crescent to full, just like the moon. Although this might not seem all that exciting today, it was a vital stage in demoting the earth from being the centre of the universe to just another planet orbiting around another star. One of Galileo's former students, Benedetto Castilli, had pointed out to him that if the Ptolemaic model was right, Venus, orbiting the earth, must always appear to us either lit from the side or from behind, as the sun supposedly orbited beyond it. If Copernicus was right, however, Venus could exhibit all the phases, being a crescent when on the near side of the sun and gibbous (between half and full) when on the far side. And this is precisely what Galileo saw.

Nevertheless, he needed more observation time to be sure. Using his old trick of anagrams to protect his discoveries (see page 194), he wrote to fellow astronomer Johannes Kepler: 'Haec immatura a me iam frustra leguntur o.y,' which literally means: 'This was already tried by me in vain too early.' No doubt this infuriated Kepler, who hated being kept in suspense.

By New Year's Day 1611, however, Venus had moved around far enough to display a crescent and Galileo could triumphantly unscramble his anagram to read: 'Cynthiae figures aemulatur mater amorum,' which can be translated, with a poetry now sadly absent from modern astronomy, as: 'The mother of love imitates the shape of Cynthia,' or, in other words, Venus displays the same phases as the moon. The Ptolemaic universe was dead.

Not everyone agreed, of course. The inquisition charged Galileo with heresy. Having been shown the instruments of his torture, he agreed to recant what he knew to be true, spending the last nine years of his life under house arrest. To be fair, the Church did finally apologise for its mistake – in 1992.

∽

If scientists fear the extreme reactions of those with whom they share their ideas, how much harder it must be to live with a great idea almost universally ignored.

∽

Sweet peas

Gregor Mendel was brought up on a small farm in what is now the Czech republic but was then Austrian Silesia. In the early nineteenth century he might have been expected to continue a family farming tradition that was then already over 130 years old.

However, Mendel was not like the other farm boys of the area. While every farmer's son had to learn what makes crops grow, Mendel had a passion for gardening and an academic turn of mind that saw him enrolled in the Philosophical Institute of the University of Olomouc. Options for an academic gardener with no money were limited in the Austrian Empire in just about every field but one. A single organisation could give a young man the time and resources to follow his dream, regardless of his family background, but it came at a cost. Mendel would have to become a monk.

Encouraged by his former physics teacher, Mendel took the plunge in 1843 and became a novice at the Augustinian Abbey of St Thomas in Brünn, now Brno, from where he was sent to university in Vienna, returning three years later as a fully fledged teacher of physics. Nevertheless, plants continued to fascinate Mendel and in his spare time he began to experiment in the monastery garden with crossing varieties of pea plant.

At the time (between 1856 and 1863), there was no real under-standing of how a plant or animal might inherit traits from its genetic parents. Indeed, the whole of natural history was in something of a fluster, thanks to the publication in 1859 of Charles Darwin's *On the Origin of Species by Means of Natural Selection, or the Preservation of Favoured Races in the Struggle for Life*, later known simply as *The Origin of Species*. Darwin himself was developing the idea of 'pangenesis', which theor-ised that the bodies of plants and animals created 'gemmules', particles that contained partial 'blueprints' for creating that creature. These gemmules, it was hypothesised, congregated in the reproductive organs where they were absorbed into the eggs or sperm.

Mendel meanwhile was patiently cross-breeding peas, 29,000

of them in total during the seven years of his study of seven specific pea characteristics. What he found was as simple as it was inspiring. In the case of colour, when he crossed a purple-flowered pea with a white pea, he didn't get offspring that were a blend of the two, as many theories of the day suggested; he always got a purple flower. He theorised that this was because the purple trait was dominant and the white trait was recessive, so purple always showed whilst the white trait was still present but remained hidden. He went on to show that each of these factors (purple or white) was carried by only one of the parents.

From this Mendel derived his 'laws of inheritance', which he wrote up as *Experiments on Plant Hybridisation* and which he read over two evenings to the Natural History Society of Brünn, an organisation he had helped to found. One newspaper, the *Brünn Tagesbote,* reported a 'lively participation by the audience' but his call in the meeting for others to take up his work was roundly ignored.

In 1866 he published his findings in the society's journal, which was distributed amongst a number of European academic institutions and he personally forwarded copies to other academics, most of whom also took no notice whatsoever. One solitary individual entered into a correspondence with Mendel and he suggested the monk redirect his work to hawkweed, a plant that can produce seeds without pollen and so is useless in experiments with cross-breeding.

Two years later the diligent Mendel was elevated to the role of abbot at St Thomas's and his new administrative duties left little time for experiment. He died at the abbey in January 1884 and most of his papers were burnt.

It would be another sixteen years before his work was re-discovered, when many of the copies of the paper he had so diligently distributed were found uncut (and hence unread) in the private and public libraries to which he had sent them. At the time, in the shadow of Darwin's monumental work, no one had been bothered with an obscure monk and his peas, yet within Mendel's paper lay the answer to the greatest weakness in Darwin's theory – proof that characteristics don't 'blend' on crossing and that pangenesis was hence wrong.

Today Darwin's theory of natural selection still forms the bedrock of our understanding of how species change, but it is Mendel's peas that form the backbone of our understanding of genetics.

✍

Not every scientist has the temperament for working alone for decades without recognition. Some need colleagues, not just for the journey but, being perhaps not quite brave enough themselves, to act as their guinea pigs.

✍

Clonidine

Whilst there are the heroic few pharmaceutical chemists who try their creations out on themselves, this is not generally something to be encouraged as the effects (see page 98) can be rather surprising and not a little alarming. Far better to test them then on a guinea pig or, failing that, your secretary.

Astonishingly this is exactly what happened in 1962. Helmut Stähle had been working on something that he had every reason to consider fairly innocuous, namely the common cold. His work at the pharmaceutical company Boehringer Ingelheim was exploring, in particular, the use of drugs that cause blood vessels to contract. In a cold, swollen blood vessels in the nose cause it to become blocked, so he reasoned that if he could find a drug to administer directly into the nose that would pass through the mucous membrane and into those blood vessels, he'd have a handy and effective way of unblocking them.

Work proceeded apace and samples of a potential new drug, clonidine, were delivered to Stähle's boss, medical director Dr Martin Wolf, where it just so happened that his secretary, Frau Schwandt, had a nasty head cold. Seeing an opportunity to immediately test the new preparation, he asked her whether she would mind trying it. As anyone who has had a heavy head cold will tell you, there are times when you'd take anything to get rid of it and so Frau Schwandt, perhaps recklessly, agreed.

Dr Wolf prepared a solution of the drug and introduced it into his secretary's nose with a dropper. Initially she reported that it worked exceptionally well, clearing her nose instantly. Moments later she yawned and fell asleep. This was not how Dr Wolf's diligent secretary usually behaved at work. She was immediately taken home where she continued to sleep for another twenty hours. Dr Wolf was not a little concerned but resolved to run some more controlled tests when his secretary woke up.

Sure enough, he discovered that Stähle's new drug was indeed a good decongestant – at very low doses – but also had the side effect of making both heart-rate and blood pressure plummet. This is what had caused Frau Schwandt's sudden and deep sleep. Fortunately she made a full recovery and her unusual brush with radical decongestion was to bring lasting effects. Clonidine was later marketed as a leading drug – not for colds and congestion but in fighting hypertension.

✑

Some of the most famous stories from science do involve a real, physical journey: Darwin, Cook and the *Apollo 11* crew, to name but a few, but one often forgotten expedition involved the exploration of a place that everyone knew about but no one thought worth visiting.

✑

Exploring the bottom

In 1872, Sir Charles Wyville Thomson, a natural history professor at the University of Edinburgh, and his Canadian-born student, John Murray, persuaded the Royal Navy that, as there was nowhere really left to explore on land, and everything worth conquering had been conquered, they might as well turn their attentions to the two-thirds of the planet that they had so far ignored – the bottom of the sea.

They called their project 'Oceanography', thereby coining the term, and they proved persuasive enough for the Royal Society and the navy to fit out the world's first purely scientific research vessel for them – HMS *Challenger*. On board this square-rigged former frigate, the guns had been replaced with a complete scientific laboratory. In a slightly sniffy history of the expedition written by the staff at the Scripps Institute of Oceanography, this is described as 'of its day rather than state-of-the-art'. This is a little begrudging from an institution that owes a third of its name and all its origins to Thomson and Murray.

The captain chosen for this gruelling voyage was the cele- brated George Nares who had made a name for himself in the Royal Navy following a little incident at the opening of the Suez Canal. Amid the jam of ships waiting to enter the canal on its opening in 1869 was Nares in command of HMS *Newport*. He was not happy with his (and hence Britain's) position in the queue, however, so on the night before the opening, under cover of darkness and with no lights, he navigated through the flotilla until he managed to anchor in front of the official first entrant into the canal, the French yacht *L'Aigle*.

At dawn the following morning the other nationalities, patiently queuing to enter the canal, were horrified to find this small British ship now in pole position, but so tightly had Nares manoeuvred that he couldn't now be got out of the way. He thus became the first captain to navigate the canal, for which he received both an official reprimand and an unofficial vote of thanks from the Admiralty. This exemplary feat of seamanship also made him just the man for the *Challenger* job.

HMS *Challenger* slipped her moorings on 21 December 1872 and set off on her 127,600-kilometre, four-year voyage of discovery, which the less-than-modest John Murray later described as 'the greatest advance in the knowledge of our planet since the celebrated discoveries of the fifteenth and sixteenth centuries'.

Murray did, however, have reason to be proud. En route around the world, the *Challenger* expedition made 362 major research stops to plumb and dredge the depths, using equipment attached to a total of 144 miles of hemp rope and 12.5 miles of piano wire. With this they collected data for the first systematic plot of currents and temperatures in the ocean, produced a map of bottom deposits (which is still the basis of that used today), discovered the mid-Atlantic Ridge and located the deepest sea trench on earth (at 5 miles' depth), just off the Mariana Islands in what is now known as the 'Challenger Deep'.

To reach this depth their 100-pound plumbing weight took 63 minutes. Whilst this was boring for the officer on duty checking that the line didn't break, he did at least have the comfort of knowing that he was basking in the world's most equitable climate – a year-round 85 degrees. This was, naturally enough, not the case on the bottom, where the pressure was a crushing 1,100 times that on the surface and barely above zero degrees Celsius.

It was the hostile conditions on the seabed that had led to the theory of the day that the ocean deeps were sterile. This was where *Challenger* turned up the greatest surprise. Thomson and Murray found that there was life all over the seabed and proved it by returning with samples of 715 new genera and 4,717 new species of ocean life forms – the largest single haul of discoveries of new life forms of all time.

Of course, writing up all these discoveries was somewhat time consuming – in fact it took 100 scientists twenty-three years to produce a total of 29,500 pages in fifty volumes, 'each as thick as a family bible'. The cost of this was covered by Murray's realisation that the phosphate deposits he'd noticed on the Christmas Islands as they sailed past were highly saleable. He claimed the island for Britain and promptly founded a mining company to exploit them, the proceeds of which paid for the publication.

∞

Perhaps the epitome of bravery in science is where someone has a potentially dangerous idea but knows that the only way to prove it right or wrong is to try it out – on themselves.

∞

Lindemann's nosedive

Frederick Lindemann was not always the most sympathetic of characters. A lifelong bachelor, strict vegetarian and teetotaller (except on rare occasions when Winston Churchill persuaded him to have a small brandy), he had a reputation as an ascetic and difficult man (see page 233). What no one could doubt, however, was that he was both brilliant and brave.

Lindemann bore no resemblance to your average academic, having a substantial private income that enabled him to live in the magnificent Aldon hotel on Unter den Linden in Berlin while studying for his PhD in physics – not the usual post-grad digs for him. Just four years later when the First World War broke out, Lindemann managed to slip out of Germany and go to England, a country he had always considered his spiritual home, not least because it was home to Wimbledon. Lindemann had the unusual distinction of being the only professor ever to play in the All-England Tennis championships there.

Life for a German in wartime England could be difficult and his attempts to gain a commission in the army were firmly rebuffed. Unable to fight, he put his mind to work for the war effort by joining the Royal Aircraft Factory at Farnborough, in March 1915. In those early days of fighting aircraft, the work of the factory revolved around experimenting with flying machines to understand their flight characteristics, improve their performance and provide pilots with vital information on how to survive in them. At this time there was one distressing problem in particular that needed to be addressed.

Many front-line pilots were reporting that their new machines could sometimes get into tailspins – spiralling down towards the ground – usually, since this was long before parachutes were issued, with fatal effect. The question was: what could be done to pull a plane out of such a lethal dive? Lindemann, who had been considering the problem, noted:

Anyone watching a spinning plane could see that the rate of turn did not increase on the way down. I concluded therefore that the lift on both wings must be equal; and this could only be true – since the outer wing is beating against the air whereas the inner is not – if its effective angle of incidence was on the high side of the angle of maximum lift, whereas the inner wing was the other way round.

This might sound all well and good to physicists and aero-dynamicists but what use was it to the poor pilots who were having to fight not just the enemy but their own machines? Lindemann might have come across as a typical academic, far removed from the practicalities of war, but he did not intend simply to talk – which was fortunate, as his lecturing style was a low mumble that most in his audience couldn't hear.

For several weeks in the autumn of 1916, Lindemann cut an even odder figure than usual at the factory, appearing on the grass airstrip each morning in his traditional bowler hat and dark Melton overcoat, with a tightly furled umbrella at his side, before proceeding to clamber into a small training biplane. Despite his poor eyesight, he was of the opinion that if he were to prognosticate on the flight characteristics of planes that men had to live and die in, he (and, indeed, all his fellow scientists) should learn to fly the things themselves.

Once he had mastered the controls sufficiently, it simply remained to test his theories on tailspin. In June 1917, he took his biplane up over Oxford and deliberately put it into a tail-spin, something that at that time was akin to suicide. As the plane spun towards the ground, dropping at over 100 feet per second and pulling 2.5 g as it spun round every four seconds, Lindemann calmly put his idea into action. If he wanted to get out of the spin, he had to speed up.

Pushing the stick forward – exactly the opposite of what any pilot would instinctively do as he plummeted towards earth – he levelled up the rudder and then pulled the plane gently up and out of the dive. This must have been a great relief, not just to Lindemann but to the inhabitants of Oxford directly below him. It was also just the sort of practical proof pilots needed. From then on they were instructed to push the stick forward when in a tailspin, saving many lives in the process.

What could have been Lindemann's last moment in fact set the seal on what would become a glittering career, although his ground crew still wouldn't give this 'German' enough fuel to cross the Channel – just in case. In 1919 he was elected Dr Lee's Professor of Experimental Philosophy (Physics) at the university that he had only two years previously dive-bombed – Oxford. By the outbreak of the Second World War, no one doubted his loyalty to his adopted home and he went on to become one of Churchill's most loyal and favoured assistants.

✑

> It is also a brave sort of scientist who,
> having seen something that looks impossible,
> says they've seen it anyway. Such a 'discovery' is
> probably a false alarm, likely to open you up to
> ridicule if you're wrong, particularly if you're
> naively wrong. How much easier it is to rub
> your eyes, shake your head and wait for
> the unexpected to go away, safe in
> the knowledge that it will almost
> certainly never pop up again.

✑

Marjorie's big catch

Marjorie Courtenay-Latimer had wanted to study birds since she was a small girl, visiting her grandmother's house on the South African coast. However, in the early 1930s the options for women in natural history were very limited, so she decided to become a nurse. It was only after her training was completed that, quite out of the blue and aged just twenty-four, she was asked to become the curator of the new East London Museum in the Eastern Cape Province of South Africa.

At the time, the museum at East London was not a prestigious institution. Marjorie spent the next seven years trying to build up useful geological, ethnographic and natural history collections, beginning by incorporating her mother's collection of local beadwork and her great-aunt Lavinia's prized dodo egg. As well as making her own collection trips to gather everything from flowers, feather and shells to Triassic mammal remains, she was keen to involve her local community, using their skills to add to her collections. In particular she befriended the local fishermen in the hope that they would report any rare birds they saw on their fishing trips as well as anything unusual trawled up in their nets.

On 22 December 1938 a call came through from Captain Hendrik Goosen of the Irvin and Johnson trawler *Nerine* that their last catch, made the previous evening in around 70 metres of water, off the Chalumna river, had fished up something strange. The timing was not good, as Marjorie still had a backlog of specimens to deal with before the fast-approaching holiday, but the fishermen at Irvin and Johnson had always helped her and it seemed churlish to refuse to go, if only to wish them a happy Christmas. She and her assistant Enoch Elias set off in a taxi.

On board the *Nerine*, Marjorie found the usual selection of sharks and rays in the hold, but her attention was immediately drawn to something else, lying in the heap of fish and weed – a dazzling blue fin. Clearing the other catch away, she later noted: 'Behold! There appeared the most beautiful fish I had ever seen . . . an iridescent blue with shades of red, green, and brown, with white spots. It was just over five feet long.'

Finding a beautiful fish was not of itself out of the ordinary but, as the crew quickly confirmed, in thirty years of fishing none of them had seen anything like it. The stocky creature had hard, spiny scales, a thick tailfin with a smaller fin protruding from the back and four heavily-built fins that looked almost like legs. Obviously the creature needed to be studied properly so Marjorie undertook to get it back to the museum. After some initial protestations, the taxi driver agreed to put the beast, wrapped in sacking, in the boot, and they headed back.

At the museum it rapidly became apparent that this was no ordinary fish. None of the books in the museum's reference collection recorded anything even resembling it. Deciding she needed expert help, she sent a letter to Dr James Smith at Rhodes University, enclosing a description and a drawing of the fish, but he failed to reply.

Matters were now becoming pressing, not least because the fish was beginning to go off and a pale yellow oil was starting to ooze from its body. Her first thought was to refrigerate the specimen until an expert could examine it, but there were only two fridges in all of East London big enough to house it. They tried them both. Carrying the fish in a handcart, she and Enoch went first to the hospital morgue, where the technicians refused to take it, and then to the food cold store, where the manager, noting that the creature was starting to go off, also quite rightly refused. At the chemist they were at least given a little formalin, so they soaked torn-up bedsheets and newspaper in this and wrapped it around the fish while they tried to come up with another plan.

Marjorie's fish didn't have a good Christmas: by 27 December it had turned dark brown and begun to putrefy, as the formalin was unable to penetrate its thick, armoured scales. Only one option remained. She called in the local taxidermist, Robert Center, to stuff the beast.

It was 3 January by the time Smith's telegram reached her.

He had been at home for the holiday and had not received her letter until his return to work. He had at once recognised the creature, but not from books on modern fish – because it was something that had previously been believed to have gone extinct over 50 million years ago: a coelacanth. As he later described the moment: 'A bomb seemed to burst in my brain.'

Smith, unable to immediately go to East London to see the specimen, wrote a series of ever more excited letters to Marjorie, asking for further details. After she sent him three of the highly characteristic scales, he wrote back to her on 7 February: 'They leave little doubt about the nature of the fish, but even so my mind still refuses to grasp this tremendous impossibility.'

By the following day he could bear to wait no more and headed straight for East London. He later recalled in his book on the coelacanth, *Old Four Legs*: 'I stood as if stricken to stone. Yes, there was not a shadow of doubt, scale by scale, bone by bone, fin by fin, it was a true Coelacanth.' He then turned to Marjorie and simply said: 'Lass, this discovery will be on the lips of every scientist in the world.'

He would certainly be proved right. Her specimen was a type of fish that had first emerged around 400 million years ago and which hadn't been seen, or so it was believed, since the time of the dinosaurs. Another would not be retrieved until 1952 and this rarest of fish would not be filmed in the wild until 1997. But here, in 1939, the East London museum finally had a specimen worthy of Marjorie Courtenay-Latimer's ambitions for the place – the most coveted and rarest natural history specimen on the planet. In honour of her, Smith named the fish *Latimeria chalumnae*. Marjorie's coelacanth remains there to this day.

෧෨

Finally we come to an example of a scientist not
going anywhere physical, not risking their life
or their reputation, not delving into horrors,
nor even just standing up for the truth.
Sometimes the bravest of scientists are those
who will go where they are not wanted, where
they are told they don't belong and then prove to
the world that they are and they do.

෧෨

The enchantress of numbers

Whilst Charles Babbage usually gets most of the credit for
the invention of the mechanical computer, perhaps one of the
greatest advances in the history of computing should perhaps
be laid at the door of a tragic and highly underrated friend.

Augusta Byron never really knew her father, the poet Lord
Byron, although he referred to her affectionately in his poem
Childe Harold as 'sole daughter of my house and heart'. When
she was just one month old, she and her mother had left the
family home and shortly after that Byron had gone abroad for
ever. He died in Greece in 1824 when she was only nine.

Augusta, or Ada as Byron had called her, was not a strong
child but during her lengthy spells of being bedridden her mother
ensured that she received the sort of first-class education that
was at that date usually reserved solely for boys. In particular
she was schooled intensively in maths by the celebrated Augustus
De Morgan, as part of her mother's scheme to ensure that she
neither grew up to become a poet like her scandalous father,
nor fell prey to the insanity that her mother, not unreasonably,
believed ran in the Byron family.

By the age of seventeen, Ada was already noted as an original thinker, so the Scottish polymath Mary Somerville arranged her introduction to the mathematician, philosopher, and mechanical engineer Charles Babbage on 5 June 1833. The two got on famously. Babbage soon realised what an exceptionally incisive mind this soon-to-be-debutante had. Having explained and discussed with her his ideas for the Difference Engine, in November of the following year he described to her a far more ambitious plan, for an Analytical Engine. Rather than being simply a calculating machine like the Difference Engine, this device would be a mechanical computer with a 'store' or memory for programs and data, and a 'mill' or processing unit to perform operations on that data.

While Babbage developed his ideas, Ada became a regular at court and in 1834 married William King, 8th Baron King. When in 1838 he became the 1st Earl of Lovelace, she gained the title by which she is generally known today – Ada Lovelace. Marriage and children did not prevent her from keeping up with the latest developments in science and literature, however, with a circle of friends that included Sir Charles Wheatstone (see page 171), Michael Faraday and Charles Dickens. Nor did she forget Babbage. When the Italian general and future prime minister Luigi Menabrea published a memoir on the Analytical Engine, she undertook to translate it into English, at the same time adding her own notes and comments, which in the end were longer than the text itself.

It was in these notes that she revealed her true genius, suggesting a method for using the engine to calculate a sequence of numbers intimately connected with number theory (known as Bernoulli numbers) as she had already outlined in a letter to Babbage, saying: 'I want to put in something about Bernoulli's Number, in one of my Notes, as an example of how an explicit function, may be worked out by the engine, without having been worked out by human head and hands first.'

Although the Analytical Engine was never built, it has since been shown that the method she fixed upon for doing this would have worked, marking it out as the world's first computer program and Ada as the world's first computer programmer. She further suggested that such a machine could be programmed using punched cards – as were then used in weaving with jacquard looms whose patterns were set using a system of punch cards and pegs. Or, as she put it far more poetically, 'The Analytical Engine weaves algebraical patterns just as the Jacquard loom weaves flowers and leaves.'

She published this work in *Taylor's Scientific Memoirs* and, with typical modesty, took no credit on the title page, instead merely initialling the notes A.A.L. Perhaps not surprisingly, Babbage wrote of her in 1843:

> *Forget this world and all its troubles and if possible its multitudinous Charlatans — every thing in short but the Enchantress of Numbers.*

Ada's story would not end happily. Her health once again failing, she was prescribed large doses of opium and subsequently took to gambling, becoming heavily in debt. By 1851 she was chronically ill with cancer and her mother was called to take charge of the household. Shocked more by the state of her daughter's finances than her health, Lady Byron refused to admit Ada's friends, including Babbage, into the house.

Ada Lovelace died on 27 November 1852 and was buried, at her request, next to the father she had never known. She was just thirty-six.

Acknowledgments

This book is a collection of scientific stories that I have gathered over the years as I went about writing books, making documentaries and advising on films. As such it includes the suggestions of hundreds of people whom I've been fortunate enough to work with along the way. I hope you will forgive me if I don't list you all.

Writing these stories has been a pleasure but each one could be set down only when the truth behind it could be found. The world is full of anecdotes, many only half remembered and some simply made up. If I were to just repeat these, I might as well have written a work of fiction and have done with it. These stories become memorable *only if* they are true or, at least, traced back to reliable contemporary sources. That has been done by Stephanie, my wife. It involves searching through an awful lot of rock to find a little bit of gold and then, on closer inspection, much of that turns out to be fool's gold. If there is any gold on these pages it is from her prospecting.

For suggesting particular stories for this book I should add my special thanks to my father David, John Lloyd and the wholly exceptional team at *QI*, Barrie Howe, Steve Maher and the E&T team at the Institution of Engineering and Technology. Once again I am fortunate to have the best team in the business behind the book too – Roland Philipps, Victoria Murray-Browne and Anna Kenny-Ginard at John Murray, my copy-editor Celia Levett, Julian Alexander at LAW and Richard Foreman at Chalke.

Finally I want to thank Connie, and now also her baby sister Felicity, who put up with having a writer for a father instead of a dad who does a proper job. We will build those rockets.

Index

Index

Index

Index

Index

Hero of Alexandria, 13, 163–5, 294–6
Herodotus, 7–8
heroin, 128
Herschel, William, 20
Hevesy, George de, 64–5
Hewitt, Abram Stevens, 180
Hiero II, King of Syracuse, 287–9
Hildebrand, Joel Henry, 71
Hirschfelder, Joseph, 71
Hitler, Adolf, 64–5, 279–80
Hodgson, Peter, 186
Hoffmann, Felix, 126–8
Hofmann, Albert, 97–9
Hofmann, August Wilhelm von, 89–90, 151
Hooke, Robert, 16, 19, 60, 201
Hopkins, Frederick, 200
hops, 150–1
horses: movement, 242–4
Hough, Leslie, 142–3
Humbert, Dr Alois, 226
Hunter, John, 275–7
Huxley, Thomas Henry, 191
Huygens, Christian, 16
hydrogen, 12

impotence: Princess Lotus Blossom's cure for, 258–9
Indiana: and value of pi, 281–3
influenza: and Katterfelto's cure, 270–1
inoculations, 107–8
'Invisible College', 19
Isaac, Rufus (*later* 1st Marquess of Reading), 118
Israel, state of, 37–9

Jackson, Charles T., 49
James, Betty, 182–4
James, Richard, 182–4
Java: beriberi in, 198
Jenner, Edward, 106, 218, 276
Jews: homeland, 37–8; and physics, 63–4
Johann Frederick, Duke of Saxony, 75
Jones, R.V., 214–15
Jupiter (planet), 194–5
Jurgens (Dutch company), 146

Katterfelto, Gustavus, 269–72
Kearns, Robert, 36
Kekulé, August, 86–9
Kelmscott House, Hammersmith, 169
Kelvin, William Thomson, 1st Baron, 61
Kempelen, Baron Wolfgang von, 260–2
Kepler, Johannes, 193–5, 298
Kevlar (fibre), 96
King, John: *American Dispensary*, 122
Knef, Joseph P., 131–2
Knerr, Richard, 188
Knight, Margaret, 157–9
Knight, Nancy, 176
Koch, Robert, 198
Kraft, Daniel, 75–8
Küchenmeister, Friedrich, 224–6
Kwolek, Stephanie, 94–5

lactic acid, 110
Ladies Home Journal, 122
Lafayette, Marie Joseph Paul Yves Roche Gilbert du Motier, Marquis de, 49
Lagrange, Joseph-Louis, 234–5
lamps, 46–7
Lange, Ambroise Bonaventure, 47
Larkyns, George 'Harry', 243
Laue, Max von, 64–5
Lavoisier, Antoine-Laurent de, 11–13, 20, 79
Lavoisier, Marie-Anne Pierrette (*née* Paulze), 11
Le Blanc, Auguste-Antoine, 234
Leeuwenhoek, Anton von, 271
Leibniz, Gottfried Wilhelm von, 24, 78, 197
Lenard, Philipp, 60–3
Lenormand, Louis-Sébastien, 228
Leonardo da Vinci, 167
Le Sage, Georges-Louis, 50
Leuvrier, Master Geoffrey, 256
Liebig, Justus von, 150–2
lighthouses, 46–8
lightning conductors, 28–30
Lind-af-Hageby, Louise, 117–18
Lindemann, Frederick Alexander (Viscount Cherwell), 278–80, 305–8

Index

Index

Index

Index